PHYSICAL
GEOGRAPHY

J. LEE GUERNSEY

Professor of Geography

AND

Director of the Science Experiment Station
Indiana State College

ARTHUR H. DOERR

Professor of Geography

AND

Dean of the Graduate College
The University of Oklahoma

Editor, Dr. Eugene Van Cleef
Professor Emeritus, Ohio State University

BARRON'S EDUCATIONAL SERIES, INC.

Woodbury, New York

FOREWORD

The science of physical geography had its beginnings in antiquity. Even primitive man must have raised his eyes and inquired "what?" "why?" The Greeks were in the vanguard of those who formulated scientific principles concerning the earth in broad terms. Nature study and the naturalist can be traced to these beginnings. As man's mind and aspirations soared, parts of the broad field of geography were separated and ultimately became such sophisticated sciences as astronomy, geology, meteorology, botany, physics, etc. This original erosion of the field of geography has led many to the conclusion that geography is a "synthetic science." And it is certainly true that geography, and especially physical geography, borrows from a great area of the other sciences. When it is realized, however, that geography spawned other sciences it seems only reasonable and proper that physical geography should use these sciences in the formulation of basic tenets.

Simply put, physical geography deals with land, sea, air, and life and their mutual interrelationships. The face of the land and its changes, the restless pulse of the sea, the invisible breath of the wind, and the silent stirrings of life which have responded to physical environment are the stuff which makes up physical geography.

Physical geography is an intimate subject. Our senses bring the sights and smells and sounds of our world to us every waking second. *Physical Geography* is designed to provide an operational framework of understanding of our physical environment for student and lay reader alike.

The perspective of millions is being broadened by travel, but "none are so blind as those who will not see." Is it enough for man to observe the majesty of a mountain peak without some appreciation of what produced its beauty? Does intelligent man observe the pyrotechnics of tornado, typhoon, or tempest without asking why?

This book provides some answers, but more significantly it provides certain insights which will lead the intelligent reader to ask additional questions. Avenues of thinking are provided which should lead the discerning reader to a greater understanding of the world about him.

The perceptive reader will find his reading more meaningful if he makes frequent reference to a good atlas, such as, *Goode's World Atlas,* Rand McNally, Chicago, 1960 (edited by Edward B. Espenshade, Jr.).

Arthur H. Doerr
Lee Guernsey

ACKNOWLEDGMENTS

The assistance of many individuals and agencies is gratefully acknowledged. The secretarial staff at Indiana State College and Miss Carol Cummings and Miss Dolores Hill of the University of Oklahoma have provided valuable assistance in typing preliminary drafts of certain portions of the text. A vote of thanks is due the Faculty Research Fund at the University of Oklahoma for providing secretarial assistance in typing manuscript copy. Dr. Harry Hoy of the Department of Geography and Mr. Don-El Steiger graciously supplied several of the working drawings.

Dr. Eugene Van Cleef, Professor Emeritus of the Ohio State University, used his great store of knowledge, vast experience, and perceptive mind in providing editorial polish. Our students have provided a constant source of inspiration, and their inquiring minds have suggested appropriate emphasis.

Many of our colleagues and associates have made suggestions and helpful criticisms. As is always the case, however, the final assessment of this work remains with the readers, and the authors bear full responsibility for sins of omission or commission.

Arthur H. Doerr
Lee Guernsey

CONTENTS

ILLUSTRATIONS

Chapter One ·

NATURE AND SCOPE OF GEOGRAPHY

To the student, geography is the study of the earth and its people. To the professional geographer, geography is this and more. It is the study of how the physical and cultural elements of the earth's surface are distributed. Using maps as a basic tool, geographers attempt to discover the interrelationships of these two elements in any given area. The focus in geography is always upon the importance these relationships bear to man. Geographers point out that no situation, social problem, or current event can be fully comprehended without considering the environment in which it exists or has occurred.

NATURE OF GEOGRAPHY

Although professional geographers approach the study of geography in various ways, their ultimate objective is the same—to understand the world in which we live. Consider the similarity of ideas among the following definitions, which are but a few applied to geography by its scholars: "The science of the earth's surface . . . a systematic description and interpretation of the distribution of things on the face of the earth," "The significance of differences from place to place," "The study of the relationship between man and his environment," and "Human ecology." A closer look at each of these definitions reveals that the core of geography consists of *man* and his *natural environment* and their spatial relationships.

The study of geography, then, cannot be limited to either physical or cultural factors alone, but rather must consist of the analysis of the relationships between cultural and physical elements on the earth's surface. In this respect, geography occupies a special place among the academic disciplines.

GEOGRAPHY AS A PHYSICAL SCIENCE Geography is a physical science because it must, by definition, deal with the physical components of the earth's surface. The entire surface of the earth becomes the laboratory of the geographer. The lay of the land, the rate of erosion, the amount of rainfall, the character of the vegetation, and the distribution of animal life are a few examples of topics which all fall within the proper sphere of the geographer's attention and study.

Within the field of physical geography are areas of specialization which are also physical sciences in their own right: *Geodesy* (the science which deals with the shape and form of the earth) is of some significance in that it permits us to understand something of the fundamental nature of the earth as a stage for man's existence. *Cartography* (the art and science of map making) utilizes basic mathematical data under controlled conditions and formulae to produce maps with predetermined characteristics. *Meteorology* (the study of weather) and *climatology* (the analytical study of the climates of the world) make use of the basic mathematical and physical characteristics and principles in association with weather prediction and analysis and the long-range climatic patterns and cycles. *Physiography* (the study of landform changes) investigates the work of wind, ice, water, and other agents upon the surface of the earth. *Geomorphology* (the study of landforms) observes rational, orderly sequences of events in nature's laboratory; similarly, landform cause and effect relationships are observable under carefully selected laboratory conditions. *Astronomy* has some relevance to geography in that the motion of the earth about the sun is of significance in determining length of daylight and darkness, seasons, time, etc., while the movement of the moon about the earth is of considerable moment in determining the rise and fall of the tides. Other celestial bodies may exert significant effects upon the sun which in turn may be related to cyclical variations in climate, cosmic rays, and a variety of other phenomena. These last relationships are not definitely established, however, and the relevance of astronomy (other than a study of the sun and the moon) to physical geography is questionable. *Pedology* (soil science) deals with the soil covering of the globe which provides the terrestrial foothold for the vegetative mantle of our earth. *Physical oceanography* (treating tides, currents, and waves) is inextricably related to physical geography because of significant climatic and landform relationships. The land-sea margin is ever-changing and the mutual interrelationships of sea and land are logical subjects for study by the physical geographer. *Biogeography* deals with the plant and animal communities extant because of climate, landform, and soil relationships. This science seeks to establish geographical limits of plants and animals upon the earth and points to potential new areas for agricultural production. *Hydrology*, which treats of the earth's surface waters and underground waters, such as lakes, springs, rivers, swamps, and ground water, is a logical and fruitful subject admissible to scrutiny by the physical geographer.

Physical geography makes a significant contribution to science in that it integrates or synthesizes seemingly detached portions of the physical environment into rational, orderly, meaningful patterns. While this book deals only with physical geography it is important for the reader to become acquainted with other facets of geography so that he may become intellectually sophisticated enough to distinguish things geographic from the non-geographic, and to assess, qualitatively, various facets of geography.

GEOGRAPHY AS A SOCIAL SCIENCE Geographers not only assess the physical environments of the world, but also direct attention to the different elements of material culture of man which give character to various areas. Man's activities are not necessarily controlled by physical environment, but they are affected by it. In one area, the environment may seemingly be an aid to man's purpose while in another, the same or similar environment may be a definite detriment to him. This is because, in each case, man uses his environment according to different conceptions of and about it, and modifies his environment through different ideas and tools. Thus it is quite possible to discover throughout the world various peoples living in what were originally similar physical environments, but who molded their areas into different expressions of material culture of their own creation. In this way, a mountain pass in one region of the world is a difficult problem for a caravan of pack animals— the most advanced means of transportation in that area. A similar mountain pass in another region of the world may be no problem for transport by airplane.

SCOPE OF GEOGRAPHY

The field of geography is generally divided into several areas for the purpose of study. These include physical (natural) geography, cultural (human) geography, economic geography, regional geography, and systematic geography. The reader may study one of these specializations exclusively, or he may concentrate on a combination of them. In this outline, physical geography is the primary focus.

PHYSICAL GEOGRAPHY In the study of physical (natural) geography, stress is laid upon the natural elements of man's environment. These include surface topography, soils, economic rocks and minerals, surface and underground water, weather and climate, and native animal and plant life. Physical geography, as an academic study, cannot be entirely free from the impact of man upon his environment. Man is seldom satisfied with his natural environment; he is constantly seeking to improve it by introducing new species, new inventions, and new ideas. The physical elements listed above have all been altered to some degree by man. Even climate, which is the element least subject to change, shows some definite modification by the works of man. For example, man's clearing of great forest areas throughout the world has probably reduced the rainfall in those areas and has allowed the winds to blow at a greater speed. Landforms have been produced or destroyed in mining, and man-induced erosion proceeds at a pace many times faster than that of normal geologic erosion. These and many other distinctive actions have given us a changeable natural environment about which the physical geographer must keep up-to-date.

CULTURAL GEOGRAPHY In cultural geography, emphasis is placed upon the study of observable features resulting from the settlement of man upon the earth. These features include population, buildings, roads, factories, farm and field patterns, mines, communications, etc. Cultural geography is one of the most rapidly expanding divisions of geography. The geographical study of cities (settlement geography) becomes more and more important as the number of people living in cities increases.

ECONOMIC GEOGRAPHY In economic geography the relationships between man's efforts to gain a living and the earth's surface on which he conducts them are correlated. In order to study how man makes a living, the distribution of materials and resources, productive activities, institutions, and human traits and customs are analyzed. Economic geography deals with the areal distribution of many widely varying activities, which include, for example, the production and distribution of the machine-tool industry as well as the grazing activities of the Asiatic nomads.

REGIONAL GEOGRAPHY In regional geography the basic concern is with the individuality of areas and the principal emphasis is placed upon the patterns of the elements of the natural environment and human activities. By using the regional technique in studying geography, what otherwise might be a bewildering array of facts is brought into focus as an organized pattern. Regional geography is generally subdivided into analyses of specific areas such as the *Arctic,* the *Central Valley of Chile* or the *American Corn Belt.*

A geographic region is an area that has one or more geographic features occurring throughout. Since there may be a large number of regional characteristics, care must be taken in selecting criteria to emphasize the actual, meaningful, cohesive relations within a region such as landforms, climate, soils, crops, industries, and people. When emphasis is placed upon such static concepts as expressions of latitude and longitude, various political boundaries, detailed information concerning elevation and area, and other geographic features of less importance, the true character of the region may be obscured. Geographers find the regional concept an excellent device for comparing or contrasting different areas of the earth's surface. Regions may be divided principally on the basis of physical differences such as climate, soil, or vegetation, or they may be divided principally upon the basis of cultural differences. Certain regions may be drawn upon the basis of both physical and cultural differences. Regions then are the logical preserve of both physical and cultural geographers.

SYSTEMATIC GEOGRAPHY It is also feasible to study topics concerning the geography of an area or of the entire surface of the earth in systematic fashion. By this method, settlements, climates, soils, landforms, minerals, water, and agricultural crops may be observed, described, analyzed, and explained. Research in systematic geography has proved to be quite successful in solving many of the problems of the modern world. Whole new subdivisions of systematic geography have come into existence as a result of ever-broadening investigations. *Medical-geography,* for example, is devoted to the investigation of the areal extent and the locational concentration as well as the environmental limits of diseases.

RELATIONSHIP OF GEOGRAPHY TO OTHER DISCIPLINES Geography, since it is both a natural science and a social science, is related to a variety of subjects in both fields.

Geography describes patterns, analyzes areal relationships, and presents data cartographically. Perhaps it is the map presentation and interpretation of phenomena presented on maps which are unique geographic contributions. Geographers are adept at correlative interpretations, but they also make significant research contributions of their own. These are most commonly made through field studies, which measure and analyze the earth's surface and the features and various phenomena which are associated with it.

STUDY QUESTIONS

1. Which of the following items are properly considered a part of physical geography? Which are a part of cultural geography?

   (a) houses   (d) bridges   (g) hills   (j) roads
   (b) swamps   (e) rocks   (h) parks   (k) factories
   (c) railroads   (f) streams   (i) hail   (l) earthquakes

2. In which area or field of geography would the following be emphasized?

   (a) Analyzing the influence of the earth's surface upon man
   (b) Studying features resulting from man's occupancy
   (c) Investigating relationships between the way man earns a living and his natural environment
   (d) Describing geographic conditions of the Cotton Belt of the United States
   (e) Analyzing the metropolitan boundaries of Chicago

(f) Studying sequent occupancy of the Great Plains

(g) Investigating malaria conditions in Panama

(h) Studying production, distribution, and consumption of Mesabi iron ore

3. Enumerate several ways in which man may alter the physical environment.

4. What is a geographic region?

5. Why has geography been termed a "correlative" subject?

6. (a) Can you delimit any regions in the locale where you live?

(b) What criteria did you use in establishing the region?

(c) Are the boundaries distinct lines or transition zones?

(d) Defend your answer.

7. What subjects related to physical geography would most logically deal with

(a) landforms

(b) rocks and minerals

(c) soils

(d) climates

(e) weather

(f) maps

(g) tides

(h) animals

(i) ground water

(j) earth's shape

SELECTED REFERENCES

Bengtson, N. and Van Royen, W. *Fundamentals of Economic Geography* (New York: Prentice-Hall, 4th Edition, 1956).

Davis, D. H. *The Earth and Man* (New York: The Macmillan Company, Revised Edition, 1950).

Finch, V. C., Trewartha, G. T., Robinson, A. H. and Hammond, E. H. *Elements of Geography* (New York: McGraw-Hill Book Company, Inc., 4th Edition, 1957).

Freeman, O. W. and Raup, H. F. *Essentials of Geography* (New York: McGraw-Hill Book Company, Inc., 2nd Edition, 1959).

James, P. E. *A Geography of Man* (Boston: Ginn and Company, 1951).

Klimm, L. E., Starkey, O. P., Russell, J. A. and English, V. H. *Introductory Economic Geography* (New York: Harcourt, Brace and Company, 3rd Edition, 1956).

Staats, J. R. and Harding, G. E. *Elements of World Geography* (New York: D. Van Nostrand Company, Inc., 2nd Edition, 1953).

Strahler, A. N. *Physical Geography* (New York: John Wiley and Sons, Inc., 2nd Edition, 1960).

Thompson, H. D. *Earth Science* (New York: Appleton-Century-Crofts, Inc., 2nd Edition, 1960).

Chapter Two ·

THE EARTH AND ITS
MOTIONS

To us on the earth, the most obvious motion of the sun, moon, and most stars is their daily east to west crossing of the sky. The sun, the moon, and the planets also drift with respect to a more fixed position of the stars. This drift is generally eastward; for example, the moon rises about 50 minutes later each day. The planets, on the other hand, move more irregularly. They drift eastward most of the time, but occasionally they appear to stop and move westward, stop again, and then resume their eastward drift. Most stars move in a fashion similar to that of the sun and moon but much more slowly. However, stars in the vicinity of Polaris in the northern sky show scarcely any movement. These stars do not rise or set for the northern hemisphere observer, but move in circles around the North Star. The explanation of these phenomena explains the relation of the earth to other parts of the universe.

OUR PLACE WITHIN
THE UNIVERSE

If we could transport ourselves outside our galaxy (Milky Way), it would appear somewhat like a great spiral nebula. From the earth, the Milky Way appears to us as a great gaseous band which crosses the sky. However, it outlines the main structure of our galaxy (Stellar Family) and in addition contains many billions of stars which are invisible to the naked eye.

The Milky Way is similar in shape to a vast lens within which the solar system revolves, or it may be compared to a vast grindstone in which every grain of sand is a star. As we look toward either side of the lens, or the grindstone, we look through only a thin section of our universe. Consequently, we see only a few nearby stars, but as we look toward the edge we look through a much thicker section and see a much greater number of stars. The so-called Milky Way thus represents the edge of the lens, or grindstone.

The Milky Way is approximately 100,000 light-years (a light-year is the distance light will travel in one year) from one end to the other. Thus, light which is traveling about 11,000,000 miles a minute takes about 100,000 years to cross its diameter. The average thickness is about 10,000 light-years.

The sun is located about two-thirds of the way toward the outer edge of the Milky Way. Even though the sun is only an average-sized star, its mass is about 333,000 times that of the earth, and the sun contains about 99.8 per cent of all the material of our solar system. The sun has a diameter more than a hundred times that of the earth. If the earth were to be placed at the sun's center, the moon (which is about 240,000 miles from the earth) would be only half-way from the earth to the edge of the sun.

Nine planets revolve around the sun in elliptical orbits with the sun at one focus. The first four planets, in order of their distance from the sun, are called the inner planets and the remaining five are termed the outer planets. Planets may be distinguished from stars by their changing positions and by their steadfast reflected light in contrast to the twinkling light of stars. The nine planets in order of distance from the sun are Mercury, Venus, Earth, Mars, Jupiter, Saturn, Uranus, Neptune, and Pluto. They all have many similarities, but the four inner planets have a higher density and are smaller than the five outer planets with the exception of Pluto.

THE EARTH AS A PLANET

The earth is the "grandstand" from which we view the solar system, galaxy, and universe. It is practically a sphere (technically an oblate spheroid) with an equatorial diameter of about 7,926.68 miles and a polar diameter approximating 7,899.98 miles. In addition, we have recently learned from earth satellites that the north pole is about 50 feet higher above sea level and the south pole is about 50 feet lower, giving the earth a so-called "pear" shape. The size and shape of the earth are fairly well known today based upon accurate measurements revealed by solar and lunar eclipses, supplemented by observations of explorers and world travelers. Additional proof of the size and shape of the earth is provided by photographs taken from very high altitudes. Since October 4, 1957, much precise knowledge about the earth's size and shape has been provided by artificial satellites launched by the United States and the Soviet Union. Our knowledge of the earth's size and shape is the basis for describing locations and distances on the earth's surface.

LOCATION

To locate a position on the surface of the earth, one uses reference lines. The equator is an imaginary reference line extended west-east around the earth which divides it into two equal parts midway between the north and south poles. At right angles to the equator is another imaginary line, which passes through Greenwich, England, called the prime meridian. The ways of describing location usually involve some combination of distance and direction with reference to the equator and prime meridian. The conventional system used is based on the division of a circle into 360 degrees. Each degree may be divided into 60 equal parts called minutes, and each minute into 60 equal parts called seconds. One degree, one minute, and one second are used in this manner as angular distances and are written respectively 1°, 1′, and 1″. Certain other grid systems may be employed by different agencies, particularly the military, but all location systems employ measurements east-west and north-south of fixed grid lines.

Latitude is the angular distance north or south of the equator. The latitude of the equator is 0°; of the north and south poles respectively 90°N. and 90°S. Longitude is the angular distance east or west of the prime meridian. All meridians indicating longitude are north-south lines and therefore converge at the poles. Since longitude is measured east and west from the zero meridian halfway around the earth, the maximum longitude is 180°E., or 180°W. (the same meridian).

Latitude and longitude measurements are not only of value in the precise location of places on the earth's surface, but are also helpful in estimating and visualizing distances between places on the earth. A degree of latitude is equal to about 69 statute miles or 60 nautical miles at the equator (that is, 1/360 of the polar circumference of 24,860 miles). Variations from those figures are slight and attributable to the slight polar flattening of the earth. The length of a degree of longitude varies from about 69 miles at the equator to zero at the poles. Degrees of longitude are measured east and west along the parallels of latitude of a globe. Their length, therefore, decreases with the convergence of the meridians toward the poles.

MOTIONS OF THE EARTH

Four motions of the earth are outstanding. Of these four, rotation and revolution exert the greatest number of geographical effects. The earth rotates on its axis which intersects the surface of the earth at the north pole and the south pole. At the same time the earth revolves in an elliptical orbit about the sun. The other two motions are mainly of astronomical interest and their geographic ramifications are unknown or non-existent.

ROTATION Everyone has seen the rising and setting of celestial bodies. What we all see is simply the earth rotating on its axis in the opposite direction from what the celestial objects appear to travel. This results in the phenomena of day and night since each point is alternately turned toward (daytime) and away from (nighttime) the sun. The eastward rotation of the earth on its axis causes the sun to make a seeming westward movement across the sky each day. A complete counterclockwise rotation through 360° occurs each day (24 hours); therefore, the earth turns through 15° every hour and 1° every four minutes approximately. All places along any given meridian have the same time; but two places 1° apart in longitude have a difference in mean solar time of four minutes; two places 15° apart in longitude of one hour, and so on. Actually the sun is a notoriously poor timekeeper and the solar time varies from day to day. To avoid the confusion which would exist with varying length of days the mean solar day, exactly 24 hours in length, has been adopted. Since apparent solar time varies from mean solar time it is necessary to employ a time equation to make the essential corrections. Because of the nature of the earth's orbit the sun is fast at some periods and slow at others. A graph, known as the analemma, is used to determine the relationship between mean solar time and apparent solar time as well as the declination of the sun. Since distant stars are not affected by the same short-comings as solar time, this star based time (*siderial time*) is used for very critical time differences and as a basic check for ordinary time systems.

The time difference between two places is used to determine longitude. Local time can be determined by noting the exact instant the sun crosses the local meridian and comparing this time with that shown by a chronometer which keeps the time of the Greenwich or zero meridian. The time difference between the two places, meas-ured in hours, minutes, and seconds, may then be converted into angular units of longitude (degrees, minutes, and seconds). For example, if the chronometer registers 4:20 p.m. at Greenwich when it is noon at an unknown place, the navigator knows he is 4 hours 20 minutes west of Greenwich or in terms of degrees, $4\frac{1}{3}$ times 15°, or 65°W. If the chronometer reads 10:20 a.m. when it is noon on a ship, the local solar time is faster than Greenwich time by 1 hour 40 minutes. Converted to angular units of longitude, the ship's position is 25°E. ($1\frac{2}{3}$ times 15°). Accurate information required for precise navigation using celestial bodies may be obtained in *The Air Almanac, The Nautical Almanac,* or *The American Ephemeris and Nautical Almanac.*

Considerable confusion would exist if every place used its local solar time. To eliminate this difficulty the earth has been di-vided into standard time belts approximately 15° wide so that the different areas in a time belt accept the time of the standard me-ridian for that belt. In theory the time belts extend a distance $7\frac{1}{2}°$ on either side of the standard meridians. In actual practice, there are many irregularities. In theory, eastern standard time is based on the solar time of the meridian for 75°W.; and central standard time on that for 90°W. When it is noon in London about 0°, it is 7:00 a.m. and 6:00 a.m. standard time respectively in New York and Chicago.

When man began to circumnavigate the globe, he found it necessary to establish a special line to compensate for the 24-hour

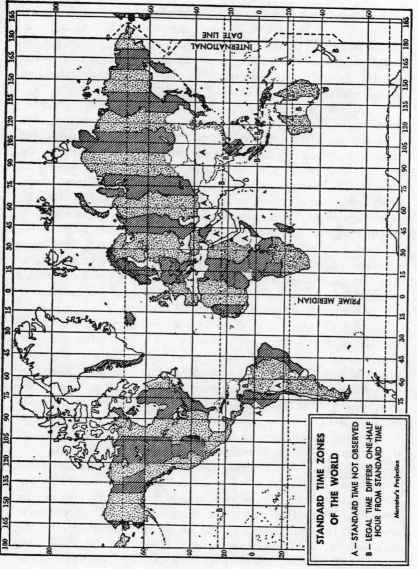

Fig. 1 World distribution of Standard Time Zones

time change. By common agreement the line known as the International Date Line, which approximates the 180° meridian, was chosen to be that place where dates change. As one crosses the International Date Line moving westward, the calendar is set forward one day. As one moves eastward across the International Date Line, the calendar is set back one day.

Several other phenomena, in addition to day and night, substantiate the fact that the earth rotates on its axis every day. One phenomenon is demonstrated by an experiment with a swinging pendulum. When a pendulum is set into motion it does not maintain the same direction of swing. After several hours it swings in a plane at right angles to its starting position. This apparent change in the direction of swing is actually caused by the fact that the pendulum plane does not change while the earth rotates under it. Another experiment reveals that a ball dropped from a tall building will not land directly below, but falls east of its starting position. The shape of the earth itself substantiates the effects of rotation. The equatorial bulge is caused by the centrifugal force of the earth's rotation. Finally, the deflections of ocean currents, winds, and storms are further proofs of the earth's rotational motion.

REVOLUTION The earth revolves around the sun. During each year the earth makes a journey of about 586 million miles about the sun in an elliptical orbit. In order to travel this distance, the earth travels at an average speed of about 66,000 miles per hour. Throughout its movement in the orbit, the earth's axis is not at right angles to the plane of the orbit, but is inclined 23½ degrees from the vertical. The earth's axis points toward the same point in space, so that in revolving around the sun the axis of the earth is always parallel to its former position. It is therefore apparent that the north pole will tilt toward the sun during part of the year, but will tilt away from the sun during the remainder of this time. This changing situation causes a changing angle at which the sun's rays strike the earth. This, in turn, affects the distribution of the sun's rays or solar energy on the earth's surface. One should also remember that the length of day and night is important in controlling the actual solar energy received at a given place on earth. However, the angle of the sun above the horizon is a principal control of temperature. The

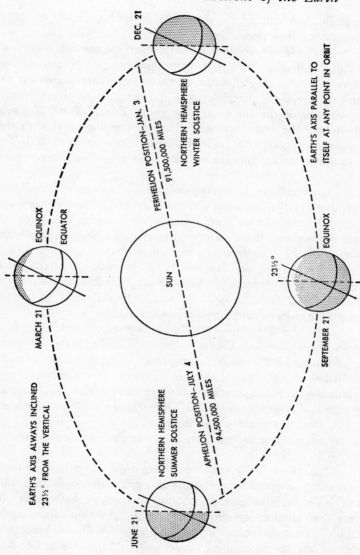

EARTH'S AXIS ALWAYS INCLINED
23½° FROM THE VERTICAL

DEC. 21

PERIHELION POSITION—JAN. 3
91,500,000 MILES

NORTHERN HEMISPHERE
WINTER SOLSTICE

EARTH'S AXIS PARALLEL TO
ITSELF AT ANY POINT IN ORBIT

EQUINOX
EQUATOR

MARCH 21

SUN

23½°

EQUINOX

SEPTEMBER 21

NORTHERN HEMISPHERE
SUMMER SOLSTICE

APHELION POSITION—JULY 4
94,500,000 MILES

JUNE 21

Fig. 2 Position of the earth at each season

change in angle during the year, together with variation in length of day, causes the seasons.

Knowing where on the earth's surface the sun's rays are vertical at different times of the year, and being able to determine and visualize the angle of the sun's rays at other points on the earth's surface is the principle used in determining latitude from a measurement of the sun's angle at noon. *The Nautical Almanac* states where the noon sun is vertical on that day, and with this value and the noon sun angle the latitude can be computed. The North Star or other stars can be used at night for similar computations.

At either vernal or autumnal equinox (about March 21 and September 21) the noon sun is vertical at the equator. An observer standing on the equator would see the noon sun at zenith, or 90° above the horizon. If the observer moves to 5° North Latitude the elevation of the sun above the horizon will decrease from 90° to 85°, and the sun's vertical rays will fall 5° from the observer. Therefore, the angle in degrees between the sun's vertical rays and a line rising vertically from an observer equals the difference in latitude between the observer and the place of vertical rays.

On about December 21, the sun is vertical at the Tropic of Capricorn, 23½° South Latitude. On about June 21, the sun's rays are vertical at the Tropic of Cancer, 23½° North Latitude. In order to calculate the altitude of the sun's rays, it is necessary to know the latitudes where the sun's rays are vertical on March 21, June 21, September 21, and December 21. Then the zenith angle equals the distance from the place where the sun's rays are vertical, and the altitude of the sun is equal to that angular distance subtracted from 90°.

PRECESSION If the earth's axis remained perfectly constant in direction, the seasons would occur at exactly the same time each year. This is not true, however, because the earth's axis wobbles with a very slow circular motion opposite to the direction of the earth's rotation. This movement is known as *precession*. Due to precession, each year the spring equinox occurs about 20 minutes earlier than the preceding year.

The precession motion of the earth's axis is analogous to the slow conical motion that a top has when it wobbles as it is spun in a leaning position. This motion is produced by the gravitational pull of the moon, sun, and planets, and by the equatorial bulge. The result is that the axis of the earth changes direction so that, if extended, it would trace a large circle within the sky in about 26,000 years. Attempts have been made to correlate the precessional cycle with long range climatic changes, but such attempts have so far proved to be inconclusive.

GALACTIC ROTATION The earth has still another motion. Each second our sun, as well as the earth and all the other planets, is speeding at about 200 miles in the direction of a point in the sky near the star Vega. This motion is due to the rotation of the whole Milky Way galaxy. Evidence of this galactic rotation is revealed by the very small changes of position occurring slowly among the stars and in the differences of velocities in the line of sight connecting the star and the observer. All galaxies seem to move in the same general direction, perhaps as a single organization of supergalaxies.

It requires one day for the earth to rotate, one year for the earth to revolve, about 26,000 years to complete one precessional cycle, and about 220 million years for one galactic rotation.

STUDY QUESTIONS

1. Explain why the shape of the Milky Way appears to be different from its true shape.
2. Why is the climate warmer in summer than in winter?
3. What is the size and shape of the earth?
4. Explain why the earth bulges at the equator.
5. How many miles is your locality from the north pole? The equator? The Tropic of Cancer?
6. When the time is 12 noon at Chicago, what is the standard time in London?
7. If it is noon standard time at 105°W. Longitude, at what longitude would it be midnight standard time?
8. How many degrees above the horizon does the noon-day sun appear at your local latitude on March 21? June 21? September 21? December 21?

9. What is the location of the opposite place on the earth (antipode) from your locality?
10. Name several effects of the earth's rotation, revolution, and precession.

SELECTED REFERENCES

Baker, R. H. *Astronomy* (New York: Van Nostrand Co., 3rd Edition, 1938).

Balchin, W. V. G. and Richards, A. W. *Practical and Experimental Geography* (New York: John Wiley and Sons, Inc., 1952), pp. 1-47.

Dunbar, C. O. *Historical Geology* (New York: John Wiley and Sons, Inc., 1949), pp. 68-89.

Johnson, W. E. *Mathematical Geography* (New York: American Book Co., 1907).

Leet, L. D. and Judson, S. *Physical Geology* (New York: Prentice-Hall, Inc., 1954), p. 9.

Lobeck, A. K. *The Earth in Space* (New York: The Geographic Press, 1929).

Longwell, C. R. and Flint, R. F. *Introduction to Physical Geology* (New York: John Wiley and Sons, Inc., 1955), pp. 9-21.

Swenson, H. N. and Woods, J. E. *Physical Science* (New York: John Wiley and Sons, Inc., 1957), pp. 37-66.

Ward, H. B. and Powers, W. E. *An Introduction to the Study of Weather and Climate* (Evanston: Northwestern University, 1944), pp. 9-14.

Chapter Three

GEOGRAPHIC TOOLS AND METHODS

The geographer's prime function is to observe, report on, and interpret the "order in the landscape." In order to accomplish this objective he utilizes certain techniques and depends upon a variety of tools. It is important for all students of geography to become acquainted with the principal geographic tools and techniques, their utilization, and their advantages and shortcomings.

GLOBES

The globe is a close approximation to the shape of the earth itself, and is, therefore, of inestimable value to geographers. It depicts distance, directions, sizes, and shapes of various land and water features accurately. Its diameter and area are proportional to the earth's diameter and area. Globes may be of several types, but most reveal both physical and cultural features. To be useful, a globe must have a locative frame of reference. This frame of reference is supplied by a grid system composed of meridians and parallels.

In spite of the fact that globes are extremely useful, their utility is reduced because of the fact that their small scale precludes the presentation of much detail. In addition, one can observe only one side of a globe at any one time and most globes cannot be easily carried about.

MAPS

A map is a representation of all, or a part of the earth's surface, drawn to scale. A map, in order to accomplish fully the objectives for which it was intended, must possess certain essentials. These are title, legend, direction, scale, latitude and longitude, and date. On occasion one or more map essentials may be eliminated if the map is being used with text material, or if usage makes a particular essential universally known.

TITLE The title of a map, like a book title is highly significant. Since maps depict a wide variety of features it is essential that the user be aware of the nature of the map. A map may show population distribution, landform patterns, vegetation patterns, or a myriad of other types of data. The user must have no doubt as to which one of these multitudinous data is being depicted.

LEGEND Legends should be clearly printed on maps to give the user an accurate indication of symbol usage. Since a legend unlocks map details, *key* is probably an appropriate synonym for *legend*. Because of widespread and common usage it may be possible to leave certain symbols out of a legend or key, but all unusual signs or symbols should be included. The legend gives clues as to the purposes of the map and should be carefully studied and evaluated before using the map.

SCALE Scale may be defined as the ratio between map distance and earth distance. Scale may be shown as a representative fraction, for example, 1/62,500, i.e., one unit on the map equals 62,500 units on the earth's surface. In addition, linear or graphic scales, and verbal scales are utilized. Linear scales utilize a line or bar of a given length to represent certain earth distances, as,

0————————1————————2 miles

Verbal scales state the existing ratio between map distance and earth distance, as, for example, "one inch equals approximately one mile." The illustrations just cited indicate three different ways of illustrating the same scale.

DIRECTION A compass rose, showing true direction and magnetic direction, is a desirable feature on every map. This compass feature can be eliminated on certain maps where parallels and meridians are properly oriented to show true direction. Other maps may have *isogonic lines* (lines of equal magnetic declination) shown on the map to make the user aware of true and magnetic north. An isogonic line of 0° magnetic declination is known as the *agonic line*.

LATITUDE AND LONGITUDE Without the locational grid system afforded by intersecting parallels and meridians, a map is almost useless. On some occasions a substitute grid, such as that utilized by the military, will replace latitude and longitude as a location aid. Proper orientation is essential to map analysis and such orientation is impossible without an appropriate grid network.

DATE Of all the major map essentials the one most often omitted is the date. Every map should show the date surveyed or the date of the data used as well as the time of construction of the map. To illustrate, a map of population density is useless unless the reader knows the date of the census data utilized in construction of the map. Maps, which would potentially have great historical significance, often are valueless because it is impossible to ascertain the date of their construction and publication.

MAP PROJECTIONS

Although a globe is the only true representation of the earth's surface it is often inconvenient to use globes because of difficulty of handling, storing, and transporting them. Although a slight rotation will reveal the opposite hemisphere, complete world distribution cannot be visible at any one time. Cartographers have been faced with the insoluble dilemma of accurately representing the entire area of a three dimensional globe on a two dimensional surface. Obviously distortion results when attempts are made to accomplish this objective. In attempts to duplicate earth features on flat surfaces, cartographers have developed map projections. A *map projection* may be defined as a systematic arrangement of grid lines transferred from the globe to a plane surface.

Some map projections are known as *geometric projections,* since, in theory, they are developed when light is passed through a globe grid upon a tangent or secant plane, cone, cylinder or other geometric figure. Other map projections are strictly mathematical in character and are not dependent upon theoretical light projection upon a geometric figure. Some of the most significant map projections, in terms of utility, are described in the succeeding discussion.

THE MERCATOR PROJECTION The Mercator projection, developed from a cylinder placed tangent to the earth's equator, is one of the most widely used world projections. Its principal attribute is simplicity. The Mercator projection shows meridians and parallels as straight lines which cross at right angles. All straight lines, *rhumb lines,* drawn on the Mercator map projection cut the meridians and parallels at a constant angle. Thus, navigation course lines can be easily and directly plotted; the use for which the projection was intended. But, because of its simplicity, it is also used for general purposes. It is unsuited for world distribution maps because the poles cannot be shown, the scale varies with latitude, and the area is exaggerated at high latitudes. The Transverse Mercator is developed from a cylinder tangent to any two opposite meridians or to a great circle drawn oblique to opposite meridians. This type of projection is especially useful along heavily traveled air routes, since, like other Mercator projections it is *conformal* (shapes are true), and scale distortion near the air route is minimal. Other Mercator-family projections use secant cylinders, rather than tangent cylinders to reduce scale distortion in a narrow band.

THE GNOMONIC PROJECTION The gnomonic projection is developed from a plane placed tangent to the earth at any desired point. The outstanding features of the gnomonic projection is that all straight lines represent arcs of great circles. It should be used for plotting great circle courses, polar maps, and astronomical maps. The scale is not constant, directions are not true, and it is accurate only at the point where the plane is tangent to the earth. The gnomonic projection is especially useful in air navigation in high latitudes, because of the ease of plotting great circle routes and the tremendous distance savings on long flights.

THE CONIC PROJECTIONS Maps of smaller areas, such as countries and states, are frequently developed from a cone or series of cones placed tangent or secant to the earth's surface. They are called conic and polyconic projections. They are easily constructed, they have a relatively accurate scale and are normally conformal. Conic or polyconic projections are not generally suited, however, to large areas as hemisphere or world maps since inaccuracy increases with distance from the line of tangency. The Polyconic projection, formerly the most-used United States map, is gradually being superseded by the Lambert Conformal Conic projection. It is a mathematical variation of the conic projection, and is especially used for maps of the United States because of its conformality and minimal scale distortion. World Aeronautical Charts on a scale of 1:1,000,000 also employ the Lambert Conformal Conic projection.

THE VAN DER GRINTEN PROJECTION The Van der Grinten projection is an especially useful projection for showing distributions, since all the world is shown on one sheet, without interruptions. It is easily read, and is a compromise between area-distorted and shape-distorted maps.

OTHER PROJECTIONS Probably the most desirable map projection for showing world distribution is some form of the Mollweide projection. It is developed mathematically by making the equator twice the length of the central parallel. The parallels are straight lines; meridians are ellipses with different foci. It is excellent for showing geographic data on a world map because areas are depicted accurately to scale. The Mollweide projection may be "interrupted" to eliminate areas which are of little immediate concern. Mollweide projections badly distort shapes in polar latitudes, thereby somewhat reducing the utility of the projection.

The sinusoidal projection is similar to the Mollweide in being equal area and having parallels as straight lines. The meridians, however, are developed from sine curves rather than ellipses. The sinusoidal projection is also useful in showing distributions, but it suffers from the same inherent shortcomings as the Mollweide.

The homolosine projection represents a "marriage" of the Mollweide (sometimes termed homolographic projection) and the sinusoidal projection. The sinusoidal projection is used for the area between 40°N. latitude and 40°S. latitude, while homolographic features are employed for the remaining high latitude regions. The homolosine projection is typically split or interrupted along specific meridians to focus attention on desired land or water bodies, but is most frequently interrupted only in the Atlantic Ocean in the northern hemisphere and in the three areas of the Atlantic, Pacific, and Indian Oceans in the southern hemisphere.

A wide variety of other map projections designed to fulfill a multiplicity of uses is available to the geographer. In fact, map projections can be tailored to fit practically any conceivable geographic use. It is important to remember, however, that it is impossible to produce a completely undistorted map projection. Cartographers

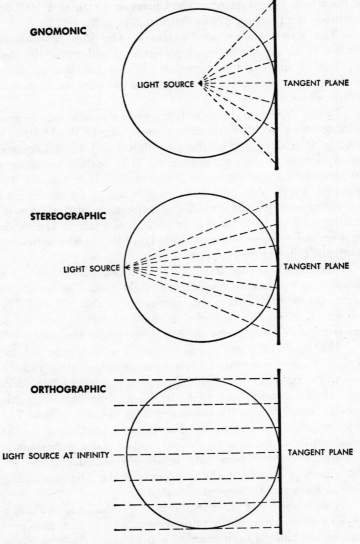

Fig. 3 Types of geometric projections

strive to make projections *conformal* (shapes true), *azimuthal* or *zenithal* (directions true), *equal area* (areas correct), and *equidistant* (distances correct), but one, or several, of these desirable characteristics must be compromised in representing the three-dimensional earth on a two-dimensional sheet of paper.

RELIEF MAPS

Maps are drawn on two-dimensional surfaces and there is, therefore, some difficulty in illustrating relief features. Several partial solutions to illustrating variations in terrain are in use.

HACHURE MAPS The hachure map is the simplest type of relief map. Lines (hachures) drawn up and down slopes give the impression of third dimension. Varying lengths and widths of lines when skillfully drawn illustrate changes in individual slopes, but do not indicate elevations. The construction of hachure maps is a laborious and time-consuming task requiring much hand labor. As a general rule high labor costs in the United States preclude the manufacture of many hachure maps there. The Europeans, especially the French, have long been known for the quality of their hachure maps.

CONTOUR MAPS A contour map utilizes lines drawn through points of equal elevation (called contour lines) to give the impression of relief. The use of a constant *contour interval* (the vertical distance between any two consecutive contour lines) enables the user to ascertain specific elevations, the form, and the slope of the land.

In the United States the most commonly used type of map to show a graphic picture of the ground surface and surface relief is the standard United States Geological Survey topographic map. The standard topographic sheet covers a rectangle of either 7½' or 15' of latitude and 7½' or 15' of longitude. If it is a 7½ minute series the scale is usually 1:24,000 whereas if the quadrangle is 15' the scale is normally 1:62,500, or approximately one inch to one mile. In recent years, 1:24,000 has become the standard topographic scale because of its greater accuracy. Five colors are used on the topographic map. Brown lines are used to show points of equal elevation, black

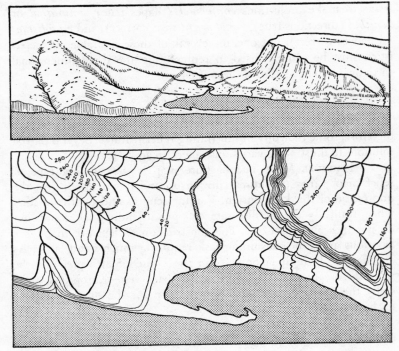

Fig. 4   Relationship between landforms and contours

and red symbols show cultural features, green is utilized to depict natural vegetation, and blue indicates water features.

SHADED MAPS Relief may be shown by the careful use of light and shadow. Slopes of hills are highlighted as they might appear in early morning or late evening light, while the other side is left in "shadow." Such a map presents a landscape picture somewhat like that which would be observed from an airplane.

HYPSOMETRIC MAPS A specialized variety of contour map which utilizes color tints between successive contour lines is known as a hypsometric map. On such a map, low elevations are normally shown in shades of green, intermediate elevation in yellow, high elevation in brown, and very high elevation in red or purplish red.

This type of relief map is frequently used for classroom demonstrations.

OTHER RELIEF DEVICES Relief may be illustrated by a variety of other methods including the relief model, profile, block diagram, and physiographic diagram. The relief model is a very effective device, since it actually shows the third dimension. Profiles show the land surface as it might appear if a giant cleaver cut through the earth's crust, and one edge was tilted up for exposure to human scrutiny. Block diagrams are drawn in such a way that the edges illustrate a land profile, while the top of the block illustrates a panoramic view. Through the use of appropriate symbols the physiographic diagram presents the terrain features as they might appear from oblique airplane views.

OTHER GEOGRAPHIC TOOLS

Many other types of geographic tools are utilized, including charts of various kinds, cartograms, graphs, and aerial photographs.

CLIMATIC GRAPH One of the most commonly used types of graph is the climatic graph, which shows precipitation and temperature curves from month to month. Such graphs are commonly rectangular in shape with vertical bars representing precipitation and a curved line representing temperature. These graphs may, however, be circular in shape.

TRANSECT CHARTS Transect charts are designed to show surface profiles and a great mass of other information. For example, in addition to showing terrain features such as mountains and valleys such charts might also show the salient elements of the physical and cultural environment in each segment of the chart.

CARTOGRAMS Cartograms are specialized maps which reduce statistical data to graphic form. For example, area circles or volume spheres might be used on a map to show varying intensity of manufacturing or any other human activity.

AERIAL PHOTOGRAPHS Aerial photographs are widely utilized for map construction and as a direct map base. Surveying and mapping based upon aerial photographs is known as *photogrammetry*. Frequently a geographer may utilize aerial photos as a base upon which data may be recorded. Aerial photos are especially well-

Fairchild Aerial Surveys, Inc.

Fig. 5   Aerial photograph used as base map

adapted for revealing patterns not observable from the ground. The uses of aerial photographs are multitudinous, and their applications are constantly expanding. A few examples suffice to illustrate their versatility. Aerial photographs are commonly used for identifying soils and landforms; for locating minerals; and for classifying settlement patterns.

Geographic tools are very numerous. The preceding discussion is not intended to be all inclusive, nor is the treatment of individual tools thorough. It is hoped, however, that the reader has been made aware of the kinds of tools which the geographer utilizes. It is through the proper use of these tools that geographers are able to interpret earth facts and to analyze their impact upon man.

GEOGRAPHIC TECHNIQUES

The geographer is first and foremost a keen observer of the natural and cultural habitat in which he lives. The field is his laboratory. By using direct observations, interviews, maps and photos, the geographer observes and makes reasonable deductions, and accurately reports them after they have been thoroughly tested. These observations and deductions reveal many different kinds and degrees of areal relationships between physical and cultural phenomena.

Since geographers are vitally concerned with areal patterns, much of their time is spent in accurately mapping distributions. These maps may be compiled from original data gathered in the field by the geographer, or they may be constructed by utilizing statistics, photographs, and accurate data gathered by others. Either method provides the geographer with a technique for reaching a relatively high degree of precision.

One of the techniques that a geographer uses most effectively is synthesis. That is, he assembles many disconnected bits of information, gathered from the field or library, and organizes them into a meaningful entity. In short, a geographer, by using these tools and methods, presents an integrated view of significant interrelations between land, air, water, biological phenomena and man's cultural environment in space over the earth's surface.

STUDY QUESTIONS

1. What are the essentials of every map?
2. What is the area of a map which is 10 x 10 inches and has a scale of 1:62,500?
3. Why is a Mercator projection map especially useful for navigation?
4. Explain why the bottom of a map is not always south. How could you have a map on which the top, bottom, and sides would all be south?

5. Which map projections would be well suited for the following uses:
   (a) To plot a great circle course as a straight line?
   (b) To depict world population distribution?
   (c) A continental map?
   (d) An equal area map?
   (e) True compass directions?
6. How may relief be indicated?
7. Theoretically where is the light source on an orthographic projection? A stereographic projection? A gnomonic projection?

SELECTED REFERENCES

Deetz, C. H. "Cartography," U.S. Coast and Geodetic Survey Spec. Pub. 205 (Washington: U.S. Government Printing Office, 1936).

Greenhood, David. *Down to Earth* (New York: Holiday House, Inc., 2nd Edition, 1951).

Lobeck, A. K. *Things Maps Don't Tell Us* (New York: The Macmillan Co., 1957).

Monkhouse, F. J. and Wilkinson, H. R. *Maps and Diagrams* (London: Methuen and Co., Ltd., 1952).

Raisz, E. *General Cartography* (New York: McGraw-Hill Book Co., Inc., 2nd Edition, 1948).

Robinson, A. H. *Elements of Cartography* (New York: John Wiley and Sons, Inc., 1953).

Steer, J. A. *An Introduction to the Study of Map Projections* (London: University of London Press Ltd., 5th Edition, 1943).

Chapter Four

WEATHER ELEMENTS

Practically all human activities are affected by weather, which is the condition of the atmosphere at a given time. Thus, a study of weather conditions is basic to an understanding of geography. Since weather changes are more rapid and more noticeable than most other elements of our physical environment, man is more aware of their occurrence. Destructive storms, high winds, heat and cold, rain and snow, and thunderstorms are but a few of the most observable weather phenomena which occur in the atmosphere surrounding the earth. A geographer also considers certain other characteristics including such elements as pressure, temperature, winds, humidity, and clouds.

THE ATMOSPHERE

The atmosphere is a *mixture* of several gases. There are about ten chemical elements which remain permanently in gaseous form in the atmosphere under all natural conditions. Of these permanent gases, oxygen makes up about 21 per cent and nitrogen about 78 per cent. Several other gases, such as argon, carbon dioxide, hydrogen, neon, krypton, and xenon, comprise the remaining one per cent of the volume of dry air. The amount of water vapor varies from almost zero to about five per cent by volume. This small quantity of water vapor, and its variations in amount and distribution, is of extraordinary importance in weather changes. Atmospheric gases hold in suspension great quantities of dust, pollen, smoke, and other impurities which are always present in considerable, but variable amounts.

The atmosphere has no definite upper limits but gradually thins until it becomes imperceptible. Until recently it was assumed that the air above the first few miles gradually grew thinner and colder at a constant rate. It was also assumed that upper air had little influence on weather changes. Recent studies of the upper atmosphere, currently being conducted by earth satellites and missile probings, have shown these assumptions to be incorrect. The atmosphere has three well-defined strata.

TROPOSPHERE The layer of the air next to the earth, which extends upward for about ten miles, is known as the *troposphere*. On the whole, it makes up about 75 per cent of all the weight of the atmosphere. It is the warmest part of the atmosphere because most of the solar radiation is absorbed by the earth's surface which warms the air immediately surrounding it. A steady decrease of temperature with increasing elevation is a most striking characteristic. The upper layers are colder because of their greater distance from the earth's surface and rapid radiation of heat into space. The temperatures within the troposphere decrease about 3.5 degrees per 1,000 feet increase in altitude. Within the troposphere, winds and air currents distribute heat and moisture. Strong winds, called jet streams, are located at the upper levels of the troposphere. These jet streams are both complex and widespread in occurrence. They normally show a wave-shaped pattern and move from west to east at velocities of 150 mph, but velocities as high as 400 mph have been noted. The influences of changing locations and strengths of jet streams upon weather conditions and patterns are no doubt considerable. Current intensive research may eventually reveal their true significance.

STRATOSPHERE Above the troposphere to a height of about 50 miles is a zone called the *stratosphere*. The stratosphere is separated from the troposphere by a zone of uniform temperatures called the tropopause. Within the lower portions of the stratosphere is a layer of ozone gases which filters out most of the ultraviolet rays from the sun. The ozone layer varies with air pressure. If this zone were not there, the full blast of the sun's ultraviolet light would burn our skins, blind our eyes, and eventually result in our destruction. Within the stratosphere, the temperature and atmospheric composition are relatively uniform.

IONOSPHERE The *ionosphere* is a thick mantle of ionized air extending from approximately 45 miles to about 200 miles above the ground. It is the most fascinating but the least known of the three strata. The word ionosphere was coined because the layer consists of electrically charged particles called ions. Its electrical properties are due to free electrons and ionized atoms thrown from the sun as ultraviolet radiation. The *northern lights* (aurora borealis) originate within this highly charged portion of the atmosphere. Its effect upon weather conditions is, as yet, unknown, although the ionosphere has considerable technological and economic importance in radio communications. Our present research program of investigating the ionosphere will increase our understanding of its influence, if any, upon weather conditions.

ELEMENTS

Several elements combine to produce a measure of weather conditions at a given time and place. These include temperature, moisture, pressure, winds, air masses, fronts, and storms.

TEMPERATURE Of all the weather elements probably the most basic one is temperature. The general distribution of temperature is based mainly upon the amount of solar energy received. Solar energy variations are primarily dependent upon the angle of the sun's rays and the length of daylight. The highest average temperatures occur at or near the equator, because the sun's rays are nearly vertical. Temperatures decrease generally toward the poles because the angle of the sun's rays becomes less with increasing distance from the equator.

Seasonal temperature variations occur because: (1) As the earth revolves around the sun, vertical sun rays change positions; (2) During summer the days are longer than the nights. Summer, therefore, occurs when the sun's rays approach vertically, and the daylight hours are longest. Winter occurs when the sun's rays strike a segment of the earth at a low angle and daylight hours are shortest.

Heat is distributed throughout the atmosphere by radiation, conduction, and convection. The sun gives off solar energy from its surface by *radiation*. This energy is absorbed by the earth and is transformed into heat. Since the earth is warmer than its surrounding atmosphere, it, in turn, radiates heat into the atmosphere. In addition, heat is transferred by direct contact between earth and air called *conduction.* The surface air, after being heated by conduction and radiation, expands in volume and thereby decreases its pressure. It becomes lighter and rises after the cooler, heavier air on either side moves in and pushes it upward. This is called *convection.* Heat transfer accomplished by means of convection occurs when surface and upper air layers are thoroughly mixed.

The temperature of the lower atmosphere normally decreases with an increase in altitude. If one ascends in a balloon through the lower atmosphere, the temperature of the air under normal conditions will decrease. The rate at which air temperature decreases with increasing altitude is known as the lapse rate. This lapse rate varies seasonally, daily, and even within a day to a considerable extent, but its average value is approximately 3.5°F. for each 1,000 feet of ascent. This is the normal temperature gradient in air which is not rising.

The rate at which the temperature of the air decreases with movement of a parcel of air upward is called the *dry adiabatic lapse rate.* The dry adiabatic rate is always 5.5°F./1,000 feet. Air that is forced downward is compressed and warmed at the same dry adiabatic rate.

Temperature distribution over the earth's surface is shown by *isotherms* (lines connecting points with the same temperature) whose value has been reduced to sea level in order to eliminate the effects of altitude upon temperatures. The general trend of the isotherms for average temperatures is similar to that of parallels. Latitude has the greatest single influence upon temperatures.

In January the highest temperatures occur over the Southern Hemisphere continents. In the Northern Hemisphere isotherms bend equatorward over the continents and poleward over the oceans. The lowest January temperature occurs over northeastern Asia.

During July the highest temperatures are over the land areas of the Northern Hemisphere. Antarctica, the largest land mass within the higher latitudes of the Southern Hemisphere, has the lowest July isothermal values. A close spacing of nearly parallel isotherms is conspicuous in the Antarctic area during July.

THERMOMETERS The temperature of the atmosphere is measured by thermometers. General temperature changes are usually measured by a *mercurial thermometer* which simply operates by mercury expanding when temperatures increase and contracting with decreases in temperature. A *maximum thermometer* is generally a mercurial thermometer which has a constriction in the base. When the temperature is lowered, the mercury column breaks at the constriction leaving the temperature indication at its highest point. The lowest temperature is recorded by a *minimum thermometer* which is often an alcohol thermometer that has an index rider or marker. As the alcohol contracts with low temperatures, the marker is left in place to record the minimum temperature.

MOISTURE Moisture exists in the air as invisible water vapor or as droplets of liquids or frozen water which we can see as clouds or fog. The amount of water vapor in the air varies greatly. When air contains the maximum amount of water vapor possible, it is saturated. The amount of water vapor necessary to saturate a given volume of air depends chiefly upon the temperature.

The moisture content of the air is referred to as humidity. The actual amount of moisture in the air (measured in grains per cubic foot) is called the *absolute humidity*. The percentage of moisture which a given volume of air contains relative to saturation at any temperature, is called its *relative humidity*. Relative humidity is measured by an instrument known as a *hygrometer* utilizing human hairs as the activating element, or a *psychrometer* which uses a pair of thermometers, one with a wet bulb and the other a dry bulb. The *dew point* is the temperature of air when saturated. Further cooling of the air will produce some form of condensation. The smaller the difference between the temperature and dew point, the higher the relative humidity.

Condensation is the process of changing water vapor to liquid water. The change from water vapor to solid is known technically as sublimation but in the study of weather is commonly called condensation because either process is part of the same major process. Condensation occurs when three sets of conditions are met: (1) There must be sufficient water vapor; (2) The air must be cooled below the dew point; and (3) Minute hygroscopic particles must be present.

The *forms of condensation* vary under different conditions and are commonly classified as dew, frost, fog, and clouds. *Dew* is moisture which has condensed upon solid surfaces of the earth whose temperature is above 32°F. Clear skies and calm air are atmospheric conditions necessary for the formation of dew. Dew forms on objects above freezing temperatures, whereas *frost* forms as condensation occurs below the freezing point. *Fog* is made up of myriads of visible minute water droplets suspended in the atmosphere on or near the earth's surface. If the fog is lifted above the earth's surface, it is termed a *cloud*.

CLOUDS A knowledge of clouds is essential to analyze weather conditions. Four families or basic groups are commonly recognized and classified according to their height and their form. The four groups are: high clouds, middle clouds, low clouds, and vertically developed clouds.

High clouds are areas of condensation which have an average elevation of more than 20,000 feet. They have, according to the U.S. Weather Bureau, the following characteristics:

Cirrus: thin, featherlike clouds composed entirely of ice crystals.

Cirrocumulus: thin clouds, the individual elements of which appear as small white flakes or patches of cotton, usually showing a glittering quality suggesting the presence of ice crystals.

Cirrostratus: thin, whitish cloud layers, appearing like a sheet or veil; diffuse, or sometimes partly striated or fibrous.

The height of the base of middle clouds ranges from about 7,000 feet to 20,000 feet. Their descriptions are:

Altocumulus: white or gray colored patches or layers of clouds with the cloud elements having a rounded appearance.

Altostratus: a gray dense veil or layer of clouds having a fibrous appearance.

Nimbostratus: a rather low, shapeless, thick cloud layer of dark gray color, accompanied by continuous rain or snow or having a "wet" appearance.

In the low cloud family are the stratus and stratocumulus clouds. The base of these clouds ranges from near the surface to about 7,000 feet. Their descriptions are:

Stratus: a low, uniform, sheet-like cloud.

Stratocumulus: clouds having large rolls, usually soft and gray with darker shading.

Clouds with vertical development are cumulus and cumulonimbus. The heights of their bases range from as low as about 1,500 feet to more than 10,000 feet. Their descriptions are:

Cumulus: dense, dome-shaped, often isolated clouds characterized by relatively flat bases with dark shading and by rounded protuberances from the dome-shaped upper areas.

Cumulonimbus: towering cumulus clouds of large dimensions with cauliflower-like tops.

PRECIPITATION When the temperature of air falls below its dew point, some of its water vapor is condensed into clouds and may be precipitated as rain, snow, sleet, or hail. The dew point of air is closely related to its humidity. If the relative humidity is high, which means that the air is nearly saturated, only a slight amount of cooling may be necessary to cause condensation. Conversely, if the relative humidity is low, a considerable fall in temperature is necessary before condensation can occur. When condensation takes place rapidly into droplets heavy enough to fall, precipitation results. Maps which depict precipitation patterns frequently employ *isohyets* (lines of equal rainfall) to show distribution.

Convectional precipitation is most common over the equatorial areas of the earth. As a result of prevailing high temperatures, most tropical precipitation is of this type. Air ascending by convection is subjected to lowering pressure as it rises. By reducing the pressure, the air expands, and as it expands it cools to a lower temperature.

Once a parcel of air is forced to rise, the degree of stability of the atmosphere determines whether it will continue to rise or will sink back towards the earth when the original cause for the rise ceases. Whether the air is *stable* (parcel will return to original position) or *unstable* (parcel will continue to move of its own accord) depends on the relation between the existing lapse rate and the adiabatic rate. If the normal lapse rate of 3.5°F./1,000 feet is applicable, rising air will be cooled at a more rapid rate than air surrounding it. As it cools, the rising air will become heavier and

sink back to the earth. Such air is *stable,* for if released, the parcel
will return to its original position. But, if the lapse rate should be
as large as 6°F./1,000 feet, rising air will find itself warmer (and
thus lighter) at any level than the surrounding still air, and hence
will continue to rise. Such a condition gives rise to *unstable* air. As
the unstable air ascends, the dew point decreases. Thus, an increase
in elevation of 1,000 feet results in a decrease in temperature of
5½ degrees F. and a decrease in the dew point of 1 degree F.
Consequently, the net result is that a 1,000 foot lift brings the air
4½ degrees F. closer to its dew point. If the air contains enough
moisture and the updrafts are strong enough, the temperature of
the ascending air will be reduced to the dew point. Further cooling
will result in condensation, the formation of clouds, and probably
some form of precipitation such as rain or hail.

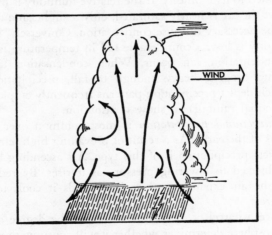

Fig. 6a   Convectional precipitation

Some convectional precipitation occurs throughout the United
States, but it is most frequent in the southern parts during the
summer. Convectional storms which develop when the air over a
locality becomes warmer than the surrounding air may form over a
city where the streets are hot, over bare fields or wherever the air
receives additional heating. Wherever the storm occurred, uneven

heating caused air to rise and cool to the dew point.

Orographic precipitation often results when air is forced upward by increasing elevations of the land. As the air ascends over topographic barriers, such as mountains, it is also cooled at the rate of 5.5 degrees F. per 1,000 feet. If the air contains sufficient moisture, and the uplift is great enough, precipitation will take place on the windward side of the mountain slopes.

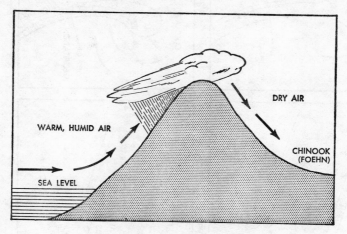

Fig. 6b Orographic precipitation

In orographic precipitation, the warm air movement may be related either to the general circulation of the atmosphere or to the circulation about a storm center. The important point is that a landform acts as the wedge or barrier over which warm, moist air is lifted and cooled to the temperature at which precipitation occurs.

Orographic precipitation seldom occurs in downpours, but usually as gentle showers. But since mountains are fixed in position, successive showers may yield a substantial total giving rise to a high annual rainfall. This phenomenon stands in contrast to convectional and cyclonic precipitation which are less localized than orographic rainfall.

Cyclonic precipitation is associated with a familiar storm type (from which it takes its name) that produces general rains over wide

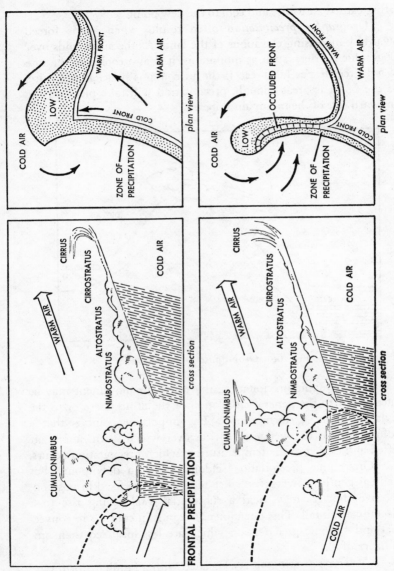

Fig. 6c Cyclonic (frontal) precipitation

areas, particularly during winter. Cyclonic precipitation occurs mostly in westerly wind belts. It is a result of cold, dense air from cooler regions meeting warmer, lighter air from subtropical areas. The two do not mix readily, but retain their individual characteristics. Oftentimes the warmer, lighter air is lifted over the cooler, heavier air. As the warm air rises, often it cools sufficiently to cause condensation and consequent precipitation.

Most of the precipitation in the United States is cyclonic or frontal. Recent studies in the interior plains of the United States have indicated that air masses and fronts are clearly the dominant factors responsible for precipitation. However, the causes of precipitation and their effects are often combined. For example, thunderstorms are more commonplace in the mountains where some preliminary orographic lifting has increased the instability of the air and, therefore, the likelihood that thunderstorms will form. Frequently, rainfall resulting from cyclonic storms is accentuated by orographic lifting. Another example of combination of storm types is the occurrence of thunderstorms along the contact zone between cold and warm air in a cyclonic storm.

Forms of Precipitation The U.S. Weather Bureau has classified all forms of precipitation into about 50 specific types of which the most common are: rain, snow, sleet, glaze, and hail. *Rain* is simply the precipitation of liquid drops of water from clouds. *Snow* is the falling from clouds of white or translucent ice crystals. *Sleet* is frozen rain formed as water falls from clouds and passes through a cold layer of air with temperatures below freezing. *Glaze* is the freezing of rain upon surface objects which have subfreezing temperatures. *Hail,* a product of thunderstorms, is composed of clear or opaque layers of ice concentrically formed by passing through clouds whose temperatures vary successively above and below the freezing point.

In measuring the amount of precipitation that falls, a funnel-like collector is used. As the precipitation falls, it runs into a small cylindrical tube. This tube has an area one-tenth that of the collector, so that one inch of rain will produce 10 inches of water in it. This enables the observer to measure successfully very small quantities of precipitation. A calibrated stick is then used to measure the water in the *rain gauge*. When snow is to be measured, the inner tube is removed, and the snow is melted to obtain the water equivalent of snow.

PRESSURE Atmospheric pressure (or weight of the atmosphere) over the earth also varies regionally. Some of these broad regional variations are related to temperature. High temperatures along the equator create, in part, a belt of low pressure. North of this low pressure belt is a somewhat interrupted belt of high pressure or high-pressure centers, and there is a similar belt to the south. In a general way, high temperature tends to produce low pressure, and low temperature, high pressure. Many of the pressure differences, however, are induced by the frictional effect of earth movements.

Weather conditions are closely related to variations in atmospheric pressure. Consequently, a knowledge of the world's distribution of atmospheric pressure is fundamental to understanding weather conditions. This is best done by cartographically representing pressure distribution by isobars (lines of equal pressure) scaled to indicate pressure in millibars. In a general way, isobars of pressure are similar to contour lines on a topographic map.

Tropical low pressures are characterized by equatorial locations throughout the year, but, they migrate south of the equator in January. Pressures are high over the continents of the Northern Hemisphere and well-defined low pressures occur over the North Atlantic and North Pacific Oceans during January.

During July, the middle latitudes of both the Atlantic and Pacific Oceans are under the dominance of high pressure. Well-developed low pressure areas occur in southern Asia and in North America. A more nearly perfect alignment of these areas along the parallels of latitude occurs in the Southern Hemisphere because of the smaller effect of land-water differences.

WINDS Winds are horizontal air movements. Winds distribute heat from the tropics to other regions, transport moisture from oceans and drop rain on the land, sweep polluted air from cities and industrial areas. In short, man would suffocate if all the atmosphere were to become dead calm. Winds blow from areas of high atmospheric pressure to areas of lower pressure. The energy is almost all derived from the sun through heating of the air and by evaporation of water. The strength of winds varies with amount of pressure change in a given distance. The earth's rotation causes winds to be deflected to the right in the northern hemisphere and to the left in the Southern Hemisphere. This deflective force due to the earth's rotation is called *coriolis force*. Wind speeds would be tremendous were it not for the drag caused by friction of the earth's surface.

In a belt along the equator where pressure change is slight, the winds are light and variable. This belt is referred to as the *equatorial low* or *doldrums*. In latitudes of approximately 15 to 30 degrees north and south, the winds are northerly in the Northern Hemisphere and southerly in the Southern Hemisphere, originating in each case in sub-tropical high-pressure centers and blowing toward the low-pressure area along the equator. The winds are strong and steady since the pressure difference is considerable. Because of the deflective effects of the earth's rotation, they blow from the northeast in the Northern Hemisphere and from the southeast in the Southern Hemisphere. They are known as *northeast trades* and *southeast trades* respectively.

Poleward from the trade winds in each hemisphere is a belt of settling air currents which correspond roughly to the high-pressure centers known as *horse latitudes*. Still farther north in the Northern Hemisphere the winds blow from the south away from the high-pressure centers. Just as the Northern Hemisphere trades are northeasterly rather than northerly winds, so these winds are southwesterly rather than southerly winds. The belt of southwesterly winds in the Northern Hemisphere and the corresponding belt of northwesterly winds in the Southern Hemisphere are referred to as *westerlies,* since within these two belts westerly winds are more common than are winds from any other single quarter. They are not, however, nearly as regular and steady as the trade winds.

Wind belts shift with the pressure belts and temperature belts. Thus the equatorial lows occupy a more southerly position in January than in July. As a result of such shifts there are latitudes that have more than one wind belt in the course of a year. For example, at about 7 to 15 degrees north and south the rising air currents of the equatorial low prevail during the high-sun period (when the angle of the sun's rays is highest) and the trades, during the low-sun period. Between 30 and 35 degrees north and south the westerlies are dominant in winter and the subtropical calms (high pressure) are dominant in summer.

Within the equatorial low pressure zone, which is generally between 5 degrees north latitude and 5 degrees south latitude, calm and light winds prevail. The weather, at low altitudes, is hot and humid and characterized by considerable rainfall from convectional updrafts. North and south of the belt of doldrums, extending to about 30 degrees north and south of the equator, are the rather constant trade winds which are warming and increasing their moisture-holding capacity. Thus, rainfall is limited in the trade wind belts except on exposed mountain slopes. Weather in the subtropical highs, in contrast with weather in the doldrums is dry and occasionally fairly cool for these low latitudes. Few clouds and a high percentage of possible sunshine generally prevail. It is within this calm belt of subtropical high pressures that several deserts are located. Within the westerly wind belts, large movements of air masses move from west to east across the continents. These air masses are largely responsible for changing weather conditions, with the high pressure air masses usually responsible for fair, clear, and cold weather, and areas of low pressure commonly accounting for cloudiness and precipitation. The polar easterly winds are warming en route, and bring only slight amounts of precipitation. When these winds from the poles arrive at latitudes of 60 degeres, they come in conflict with relatively warmer westerly winds and this interaction frequently produces air masses that dominate weather conditions between 40 and 60 degrees north and south latitude.

The circulation of the earth's atmosphere in the previously described classical model can be thought of as starting at the equator. Since more of the sun's energy is received near the equator than farther north and south, greater heat occurs there, and as a result the air rises. The warm air ascends at the equator, but when it reaches about 30 degrees latitude, it has lost enough heat so that it tends to sink. The down-moving air divides at the earth's surface; a part moving back toward the equator as trade winds; another part

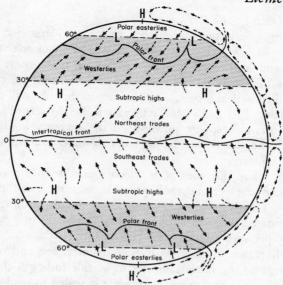

Fig. 7 Idealized wind and pressure diagram on rotating homogeneous earth

moving toward the poles as westerlies. At the poles a mass of cold air builds up and blows equatorward. Surface air warms sufficiently by the time it reaches approximately 60 degrees latitude to produce a low pressure zone known as the subpolar low. Air moving from the subtropical high towards the subpolar low is deflected by coriolis force to produce the westerlies. This pattern of winds and pressures is known as the planetary wind system. However distribution of land and water spoils the symmetry of this idealized planetary wind and pressure model.

Another disruption of the prevailing westerlies is a high velocity stream of air which blows generally from west to east called the *jet stream*. In winter, the jet stream is centered around 30° to 35° North; in summer it moves north and averages around 40° to 50° North. It is normally about 100 to 300 miles wide, several thousands of feet thick, and has velocities of 200 to 400 miles per hour. Jet streams probably also occur in both higher altitudes and in Southern Hemisphere latitudes, and occasionally blow in northerly or southerly directions.

Atmospheric pressure is measured by a barometer. A *mercurial barometer,* which consists of a glass tube about one yard long with one end sealed and the other end open, is the most accurate type. This tube is filled with mercury and inverted into a vessel partially filled with mercury. The mercury in the tube will normally drop to about 29.92 inches, but will vary in height according to the weight of the atmosphere pressing on the mercury in the vessel. Therefore, the length of the mercury column will indicate the atmospheric pressure.

For many purposes, it is inconvenient to use a mercurial barometer. A cheaper and more portable instrument is the *aneroid barometer.* This instrument depends upon the air pushing upon a soft, airtight, metal box from which the air has been partly evacuated. When the pressure increases, the box is compressed, and when the pressure decreases, the box expands. A pointer, one end connected to the box, and the other pointing to a scale indicates the atmospheric pressure. If an aneroid barometer is scaled to read elevation instead of pressure, it is called an *altimeter.*

Wind direction is indicated by a freely exposed wind *vane.* It is a simple device which points into the wind, and rotates only as the wind changes direction. Thus, a wind vane which points south indicates a south wind. The velocity of the wind is recorded by an *anemometer.* The cup anemometer is most commonly used. It is an instrument which has a set of cups mounted on a vertical axis. The stronger the wind blows, the faster the cups rotate and by counting the rotations in a given period of time, the wind velocity can be determined.

AIR MASSES The westerly wind belt has secondary patterns of air circulation superimposed upon it called air masses. *Air masses* are large bodies of air which are horizontally uniform. Within these air masses the temperature, humidity, and pressure characteristics are about the same as other areas of the same air mass.

The air within an air mass has characteristics like those of its source. If, for example, the source region is warm and moist, the air mass likewise is warm and moist. Air masses are, therefore, classified according to their source region. Air masses passing over the United

States are either tropical or polar. If the source region is over water, they are called maritime; if over land, they are called continental.

After the air masses are formed, they eventually begin to move because of variations in temperature and pressure. These air masses are usually several miles thick and hundreds of miles in diameter. They travel hundreds of miles without losing their original characteristics, and are modified very slowly. The degree to which air masses become modified depends upon the length of time the air remains in the source region and the temperature contrasts between the air and the underlying earth's surface.

Weather conditions of the United States are primarily caused by changes in the movement of air masses. Continental polar air masses from Canada usually move eastward across the Great Plains and northeastward across the Interior Plains and Appalachian Mountains. Maritime tropical air originates in the Gulf of Mexico and moves generally northeastward. The meeting of these two contrasting air masses establishes the basic pattern of fronts in the areas east of the Rocky Mountains. The areas of the United States west of the Rocky Mountains are largely dominated by Maritime Pacific air masses.

FRONTS The zone of contact between the two air masses is called a *front*. A *cold front* is the zone where cold air is displacing warm air, whereas a *warm front* is the zone where warm air is displacing cold air.

Of primary importance in producing weather changes in the United States are the changing pressures. A mass of warm light air has a low pressure while, conversely, a mass of heavier cold air has a high pressure. Such air masses are referred to as *Highs* and *Lows*.

A high usually develops as a tongue of cold polar air bulging between two areas of warmer air. It pushes in under the warm air and the cold air of the high moves outward in all directions. In the winter, highs often account for cold waves. Because the high is a cold mass of air moving outward toward lower pressures and warmer temperatures, it generally has no precipitation occurring within it. However, a cold air mass may cause precipitation by underrunning and lifting warmer air, forcing it to cool below the dew point temperature.

The passage of a cold front is normally marked by an abrupt reduction of temperature, a shift in the wind, an abrupt rise in pressure, and often squally weather. When a cold front displaces moist, unstable air, heavy precipitation frequently occurs. When it displaces moist, stable air, the weather will normally be characterized by lighter precipitation. When the front moves rapidly, the weather will usually become clear and cooler after it passes. Clearing will be slow for a front moving slowly.

Warm fronts have gentle slopes; consequently, they affect weather far in advance of the frontal position at the earth's surface. The amount of moisture in the air determines whether or not precipitation will occur. The passage of a warm front is marked by a rise in temperature, a fall in pressure, a shift in the wind, and cloudiness usually decreases or completely disappears.

Cold fronts normally move faster than warm fronts and frequently overtake the warm fronts. The warm air is then lifted since it is less dense. The new front formed is termed an *occluded front.*

STORMS Thunderstorms are fairly common in humid areas. To produce an appreciable amount of precipitation part of the air mass has to be unstable. Once strong vertical motions are started in unstable air, thunderstorms may begin to form. They commonly account for heavy downpours of precipitation.

A number of other storms also strongly affect weather conditions. Two localized storms which adversely affect weather in various parts of the United States are *tornadoes* and *hurricanes.*

Tornadoes extend over a very narrow area, but are violent and destructive, localized storms. The storm is a whirling funnel of air having a very low pressure. The width of the storm at the ground averages about 300 yards, and it generally moves along the ground from the southwest at about 30 or 40 miles per hour. The average tornado's path is about 16 miles long. Wind velocities, which rotate in a counterclockwise direction in the northern hemisphere, frequently are as high as 200 miles per hour or more within the tornado. Two weather conditions usually necessary for tornado development are: (1) warm, humid air flowing into a low pressure area from the southwest, and (2) a cold front advancing rapidly from the west. Tornadoes occur most frequently during late afternoon or early evening of the early summer months in the Great Plains and Interior Plains within the United States. In a building, the best place for safety is the southwest corner of a basement.

Hurricanes originate within 5 degrees to 10 degrees of the equatorial calm belt during the late summer months. The main condition necessary for a hurricane is warm, moist air rising and setting up a high wind. Hurricanes are normally more than 300 miles in diameter, and usually move along a path over the North Atlantic Ocean at a velocity of from 10 to 30 miles per hour. The trade winds often push hurricanes westward across the Bahamas and toward Florida and the Gulf of Mexico, but a hurricane's path is capricious. Some hurricanes strike Mexico, but others turn north and move along the Atlantic Coast, and still others, for no apparent reason, move northwestward. A typical hurricane has a life span of about eight to ten days, and blows with wind velocities of more than 75 miles per hour. The strength and path of hurricanes is apparently related to air currents associated with the jet stream. A hurricane does not cover nearly as large an area as most ordinary lows, nor can it match the intensive fury of a tornado, but it is more dangerous primarily because of the great waves which it piles up from the sea. Of the total number of hurricanes per year, about two, on the average, bring destruction to some part of the southeastern coast of the United States. The Pacific counterpart of the hurricane is the *typhoon;* in the Indian Ocean it is termed a *cyclone;* in the Philippines a *baguio;* and in Australia a *willy-willie.*

WEATHER FORECASTING

Weather forecasting is a mixture of art and science and in some ways, as in medicine, is similar to the diagnosis and prognosis of a disease by a physician. Both fields of science require a number of observations. In both sciences an accurate analysis or diagnosis is necessary prior to the forecast or prognosis. It is impossible, however, to isolate weather phenomena and conduct controlled experiments. Rather, it is necessary to study atmospheric data from hundreds of places simultaneously.

In order to evaluate information gathered from atmospheric

measurements, weather forecasters must have a clear and concise mental picture of each weather phenomenon. This picture is secured from the daily weather map, a *synoptic chart,* which shows existing weather conditions over the entire United States.

A *weather map* is an important tool for geographers. A succession of three or four maps presents a continuous picture of weather changes. Weather forecasters are able to determine the speed of air masses and fronts; to determine whether an individual pressure area is deepening or becoming shallow and whether a front is increasing or decreasing in intensity. They are also able to determine whether an air mass is retaining its original characteristics or taking on those of the surface over which it is moving. Thus, a most significant function of the map is to reveal a synoptic picture of conditions in the atmosphere at a given time.

All students of geography should be able to interpret a weather map accurately. Weather maps contain an enormous amount of information about weather conditions existing at the time of observation over a large geographical area. They reveal in a few minutes what otherwise would take hours to describe. The United States Weather Bureau issues information about approaching storms, floods, frosts, drouths, and all climatic conditions in general. Twice a month it issues a 30-day "outlook" which is a rough guide to weather conditions likely to occur over broad areas of the United States. These 30-day outlooks are based largely upon an analysis of the upper air levels which often set the stage for the development of air masses, fronts, and storms.

Considerable effort is being exerted today to achieve more accurate weather predictions. With the use of electronic instruments and earth satellites, enormous gains have taken place recently in identifying and tracking storms over regions which have but few meteorological stations. Extensive experiments are also in progress for weather modification studies. But the limitations of weather modification have prevented meteorological results except in the seeding of super-cooled, upslope mountainous winds which have produced additional orographic precipitation on the windward side of mountain ranges. Nevertheless, they have provided a clearer understanding of the fundamentals of weather elements.

STUDY QUESTIONS

1. Name and describe the three atmospheric layers.
2. Name an instrument used to measure:
   (a) temperature   (c) pressure   (e) wind direction
   (b) humidity   (d) wind velocity   (f) precipitation
3. What areas receive most of the rainfall as convectional precipitation? as orographic? as cyclonic?
4. At what elevation would condensation take place if air at 70°F. were lifted orographically from sea level to 10,000 feet, and the dew point temperature were 25°F.?
5. Why are the areas of subtropical high pressures usually characterized by low precipitation?
6. Contrast the characteristics of a warm and cold front.
7. Differentiate between a tornado and a hurricane.
8. What are the principal sources of air masses passing over the United States?
9. Under what circumstances are trade winds moisture bearing winds and under what conditions are they desiccating winds?
10. What are the four major cloud divisions?
11. What is the principal factor responsible for the development of the generalized wind system?

SELECTED REFERENCES

Berry, F. A., Bollay, E. and Beers, N. R. *Handbook of Meteorology* (New York: McGraw-Hill Book Co., Inc., 1945).

Blair, T. A. and Fite, R. C. *Weather Elements* (Englewood Cliffs, N.J.: Prentice-Hall, Inc., 1957).

Donn, W. L. *Meteorology* (New York: McGraw-Hill Book Co., Inc., 2nd Edition, 1951).

Flora, S. *Hailstorms* (Norman: University of Oklahoma Press, 1956).

Flora, S. *Tornadoes* (Norman: University of Oklahoma Press, 1955).

Haynes, B. C. *Meteorology for Pilots* (Washington: United States Government Printing Office, 1943).

Petterssen, S. *Introduction to Meterology* (New York: McGraw-Hill Book Co., Inc., 2nd Edition, 1943).

Taylor, G. F. *Elementary Meteorology* (New York: Prentice-Hall, Inc., 1954).

Trewartha, G. T. *An Introduction to Weather and Climate* (New York: McGraw-Hill Book Co., Inc., 3rd Editions, 1954).

Chapter Five ·

CLIMATES

Of all the geographical elements to which man is subjected, probably none is more fundamental in the study of geography than climate. Climate plays a role in the food we eat, the clothes we wear, the amount of energy we possess, the kind of houses we build, and in general establishes limits on what we do. No person can escape its numerous impacts. Climate also affects the natural vegetation, soils, agricultural land use, and settlement. Regions of unbalanced climates are often unprogressive, whereas those possessing well balanced climates generally have advanced civilizations. Since man is so greatly influenced by climate, an understanding of its basic principles is essential to our own purpose.

CLIMATIC INFLUENCES

Weather is the state of the atmosphere at any given time. *Climate* is a composite of weather conditions over a long period of time. All climatic conditions are the result of such basic elements as: (1) latitude; (2) the distribution of land and water bodies; (3) ocean currents; (4) altitude; (5) topography; (6) winds and air masses; and (7) storms. These seven influences, together with several minor ones, form a variety of climatic regions.

LATITUDE Our sun is the only important source of heat for the earth. The amount of radiant energy received on the horizontal surface of the earth from the sun is called *insolation*. Amounts of insolation vary in response to changes in angle of the sun's rays and length of day. Latitude is the most important factor which determines the variation in insolation received at various places on the earth's surface. Sun rays which strike the earth at a low angle are dispersed over a wide surface area. The higher the latitude the thicker the section of the earth's atmosphere through which the rays must pass. These low angle sun rays become less effective heating agents the nearer the poles are approached. Since the *average* length of daylight and darkness is the same everywhere, duration of night and day is not a significant factor in the amount of insolation received during the entire year, but it is important in causing summers to be warmer and winters to be colder in the middle and higher latitudes than in low latitudes. At the equator the length of daylight and darkness are always equal.

Most geographers assume that the amount of solar energy received at the earth's surface is fairly constant even though the sun is a variable star. In addition, the distance between the earth and sun varies from approximately 91.5 million miles to about 94.5 million miles each year, which produces minor variations in solar insolation. Certain climatologists attribute major cyclical variations in climate to the variability of radiant energy from the sun.

LAND AND WATER One characteristic which differentiates the earth from other planets is the great sea which covers 71% of the surface. Mars seems to have ice caps, some moisture, but no sea. Apparently, Mercury has no atmosphere at all. Venus is surrounded by a dense atmosphere which probably contains neither oxygen nor water. All other planets are too cold to have a sea. The earth's seas serving as reservoirs of moisture and ameliorating influences upon temperature are of major significance in the pattern of earth climates.

Water bodies heat and cool more slowly than land areas mainly because of: (1) the greater specific heat of water; (2) the deeper penetration of heat and light into water; (3) the higher reflection of heat from the water surface; and (4) the circulation of water. Water bodies become stabilizers of temperatures, which directly cause atmospheric temperatures over water to be more uniform than those over land areas. Consequently, regions which are located at great distances from oceans are likely to have hotter summers and colder winters than coastal regions in the same latitude. Coastal or marine climates tend to have fewer temperature extremes.

OCEAN CURRENTS Closely associated with oceans as climatic influences are ocean currents. The Atlantic Ocean and Pacific Ocean each has two systems of currents, a northern one and a southern one. Ocean currents may be classified according to temperature, as warm or cold. They are also classified by position, as surface currents or deep sea currents. A general surface movement of water, which has no sharp boundaries, is known as a *drift*. A current whose waters are distinctive is called a *stream*.

In the Northern Hemisphere surface ocean currents move clockwise, while in the Southern Hemisphere the motion is counterclockwise. These motions result from the deflective force of the earth's rotation. Ocean currents also have a definite circulation pattern because friction by winds moving over ocean waters causes a relatively thin layer of surface water to move slowly with the winds. Other causes for ocean currents are differences in density due to variations in temperature, evaporation, and salinity. Ocean currents moving from low and warm latitudes to higher latitudes are generally warmer than surrounding waters. Warmer waters normally increase temperatures of air which pass over them and thereby, indirectly moderate climates of surrounding land masses which have onshore winds. Cold ocean currents moving equatorward from higher latitudes generally reduce temperatures of adjacent land areas in the same way.

Mere proximity of a warm or cold ocean current to coastal regions is not enough to produce any marked effect on coastal climates. Only if winds or air masses carry marine effects inland will climates be markedly affected. Thus, sometimes deserts extend to the ocean, and areas bordering warm currents are cold when prevailing winds blow from the land. Where cold and warm currents meet there are frequent fogs caused by the contact of cold and warm air masses.

As the westerly wind belt moves across the North Atlantic Ocean, it brings warming influences poleward by the *Gulf Stream*. Mid-latitudinal climatic conditions are brought to subpolar areas by the Gulf Stream and the *North Atlantic Drift*. A portion of the North Atlantic Drift, accompanied by generally westerly winds moderates the climates of the northwest European countries while another part, termed the *Canary Current,* turns southward along the western coast of Africa. The waters are returned to the Caribbean

Sea by the *North Equatorial Current*.

In the South Atlantic Ocean, the *Brazilian Current* moves poleward along the east coast of Brazil to the westerly wind belt. The waters follow the *West Wind Drift* to Africa where they turn northward as the *Benguela Current*. They are returned to Brazil by the *South Equatorial Current*. Each ocean has a system of ocean currents which circulate in a similar manner; only the names of the currents and drifts are changed.

ALTITUDE Altitude is commonly recognized as strongly affecting both temperatures and rainfall. Air becomes cooler by an average of about $3\frac{1}{2}$°F. per 1,000 feet rise in elevation of the land. Radiant energy from the sun penetrates the thin, outer layers of the atmosphere and is effectively absorbed at the earth's surface. Since the atmosphere receives most of its heat from the earth, temperatures decrease with increasing elevations. In stable air, heat is transferred by radiation and conduction while in unstable air, convection also distributes heat through a portion of the atmosphere.

Tropical highlands, like those in Mexico, are often cooler than mid-latitudinal plains. For example, Mexico City at about 7,500 feet above sea level, has an average annual temperature of about 60°F. El Paso, Texas, which is about 1,000 miles north of Mexico City has an average annual temperature of about 63°F. Even though Mexico City has a more equatorward location its higher elevation produces a lower temperature.

The higher the altitudes, depending on wind direction, the greater the precipitation. For example, the total precipitation of the Black Hills is markedly greater than that of the surrounding areas of the Great Plains. The combination of contrasting temperatures and precipitation of higher altitudes often causes marked zones of natural vegetation and crop zones which are vertically arranged along common altitudes.

TOPOGRAPHY Sometimes topography exercises important controls over climate by causing orographic precipitation on windward slopes, and in producing dry leeward slopes. It is also important in affecting the paths of air masses and storms. For example, the Rocky Mountains usually prevent polar air from reaching the west coast of the United States. This barrier effect accounts, in part, for the higher minimum temperatures in comparable latitudes on the west coast.

As air is forced over mountains, it cools at the adiabatic rate of 5.5°F. per 1,000 feet until the dew point temperature is reached. The cooling is reduced to about 3°F. per 1,000 feet in the area of condensation. As the air descends on the leeward slope, it warms by 5.5°F. per 1,000 feet. When the air is heated, its capacity for holding moisture is increased. Air descending the leeward slopes of mountain barriers is heated by compression creating warm drying winds known as *chinook* winds in North America and *foehn* winds in Europe. Some deserts, such as Death Valley, California, are maintained in a continuous dry state because all winds move into the area as down-slope winds.

WINDS AND AIR MASSES Winds blowing from tropical latitudes generally cause higher temperatures within the areas into which they are moving. They tend to yield less precipitation, however, because the increased temperature raises the moisture holding capacity of the air. In contrast, winds blowing from higher to lower latitudes induce lower temperatures and more precipitation.

Local winds, such as monsoon circulations, land and sea breezes, mountain and valley breezes, also produce temperature and precipitation changes. For example, at night along a seacoast the air over the land tends to become colder than over the water. In contrast, during the daytime the air over the land tends to have a higher temperature than that over the water. As a result of temperature and pressure changes, a land breeze prevails at night (when the air over the land is colder and the pressure higher than that over the water). A sea breeze blows during the daytime.

The effect of air moving over continents in large masses is clearly the dominant cause of weather changes in mid-latitudes. Fronts, which result from the meeting of two different air masses, have been shown to cause most precipitation within humid continental climates.

STORMS Storms are locally important in producing various weather changes and thus become a climatic influence. They are probably the least predictable climatic influence. Thunderstorms associated with fronts and local convection are great generators of precipitation. Oftentimes great turbulences send large quantities of air aloft. In fact, pilots have experienced several thousands of feet rise during a thunderstorm when the aircraft was in a diving position.

Tropical storms, which originate over water, bring heavy rainfall to coastal regions of tropical and subtropical latitudes. Frontal and convectional thunderstorms are common to most areas of the westerly wind belts of both the northern and southern hemispheres. They are scarcely experienced except in the mid-latitudes. Strong anticyclones frequently bring blizzard conditions to the higher latitudes.

MAN'S INFLUENCE UPON CLIMATE Man's interference with nature is creating climatic changes. Creation of artificial lakes, changing of river courses, large-scale clearing of trees and recent reforestation, pollution of air in industrial and municipal areas, and increased radiation by atomic experiments have all created small but important climatic changes. Significant local climatic changes have been brought about by the cloud seeding of air on windward slopes of mountains. Further experimentation in weather modification will certainly take place. Man probably never will become a climatic "control," but as during recent decades he will certainly continue to be an important "influence" upon climatic conditions.

CLIMATIC REGIONS

The broad outlines of climatic patterns may be deduced from a knowledge of climatic influences. Climatic patterns are not accidental, but rather result from the interaction of all climatic influences. Various classifications of climates are used, since geographers do not agree upon any single system. Students of geography should not be confused by this, however, because there is basic agreement. Points of disagreement generally center around names and boundaries of transition zones. All classifications have climates grouped with respect to significant features of seasonal patterns, departures from certain standards and fluctuations, as well as average annual characteristics.

All available information about weather conditions forms

the basis of climatic classifications. Temperatures and precipitation are considered to be the two main climatic elements; nevertheless, significant data about winds, cloudiness, sunshine, and humidity are also used when available. In many areas, however, temperature and precipitation are the only climatic data available. In such situations they become the basis of climatic classification and enable geographers to visualize the global distribution within a comprehensive framework.

The problem of finding a satisfactory climatic classification is a difficult one. Many schemes for classifying climates have been proposed but none is satisfactory for *all* requirements. One basic difficulty is inherent in the fact that there are few sharp boundaries between climatic regions. Except for coastlines and mountain crests, climatic regions gradually change from one to another. A fixed boundary which separates natural climatic regions becomes an arbitrary one. This is true, in part, because of the seasonal shifts which occur in the angle of the sun's rays and the circulation of the wind belts. To be functional the climatic classification has to be based upon mean values of climatic elements rather than upon specific changes.

The climatic classification used in this book is a slight variation of one developed by the late W. Koeppen and modified by Glenn T. Trewartha. Trewartha's is one of the most widely used climatic classifications. Other classifications, such as those developed by C. Warren Thornthwaite, however, have merit, too.

In the *Trewartha climatic system,* six major climatic groups are identified. Four of these groups are based on temperature, the fifth on rainfall, the sixth on vertical zonation. The six groups are: (1) Tropical rainy (A), with all monthly mean temperatures above approximately 65°F.; (2) Dry (B), with deficient rainfall, and evaporation exceeding the precipitation received; (3) Warm temperate (C), called humid mesothermal by Trewartha, with at least one month below 65°F., but all months above 32°F.; (4) Cold temperate (D), termed humid microthermal by Trewartha, with at least one month below 32°F., and with at least one month over 50°F.; (5) Polar (E), with all months below 50°F., and (6) Undifferentiated highlands (H).

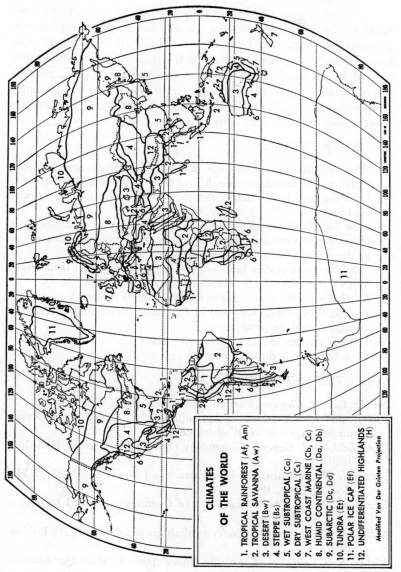

Fig. 8 Climates of the world

CLIMATES
OF THE WORLD

1. TROPICAL RAINFOREST (Af, Am)
2. TROPICAL SAVANNA (Aw)
3. DESERT (Bw)
4. STEPPE (Bs)
5. WET SUBTROPICAL (Ca)
6. DRY SUBTROPICAL (Cs)
7. WEST COAST MARINE (Cb, Cc)
8. HUMID CONTINENTAL (Da, Db)
9. SUBARCTIC (Dc, Dd)
10. TUNDRA (Et)
11. POLAR ICE CAP (Ef)
12. UNDIFFERENTIATED HIGHLANDS (H)

Modified Van Der Grinten Projection

Since various subdivisions are also recognized, twelve basic types are identified. In the four groups, based upon temperatures, precipitation forms the basis of most subdivisions, whereas both temperature and amounts of rainfall are significant factors considered in subdividing dry climates. In addition, specific months above certain temperatures, annual temperature ranges, maximum temperatures, rainfall distribution, and minimum temperatures are other factors utilized as the basis for subtypes.

STUDY QUESTIONS

1. What are the major climatic influences which characterize your local area? What interrelationships of these factors are evident?
2. Give the principal weather elements upon which climatic regions are based.
3. How has climate established limits upon what you can accomplish?
4. What is the outstanding characteristic of all tropical climates? of all dry climates? of all polar climates?
5. Why do water bodies heat and cool more slowly than land areas?
6. What forces affect the circulation of ocean currents?
7. In what ways do ocean currents modify or affect climates?
8. Explain why Mexico City and El Paso have approximately the same average annual temperature.
9. In what ways do storms influence climates?
10. How has man modified climate?

SELECTED REFERENCES

Brooks, C. E. P. *Climate* (London: Ernest Benn, Ltd., 1929).

Climate and Man Yearbook of Agriculture, 1941, United States Department of Agriculture, Washington, D.C.

Critchfield, H. J. *General Climatology* (New York: Prentice-Hall, Inc., 1960).

Haurwitz, B. and Austin, J. M. *Climatology* (New York: McGraw-Hill Book Co., Inc., 1944).

Kendrew, W. G. *The Climates of the Continents* (Oxford University Press, 4th Edition).

Miller, A. A. *Climatology* (London: Methuen and Co., Ltd., 7th Edition, 1950).

Visher, S. S. *Climatic Atlas of the United States* (Cambridge: Harvard University Press, 1956).

Chapter Six

CLIMATIC REGIONS

The geographical distribution of distinct climatic regions is the result of the interplay of weather elements and climatic influences. They produce combinations known as *climatic types*. These are given consideration in the following pages.

TROPICAL RAINY CLIMATES (A)

Tropical climates are frost-free throughout the year. Seasons are based upon distribution and amounts of rainfall rather than temperature. Some tropical areas have large amounts of evenly distributed rainfall; other areas have high totals but uneven distributions; some areas have only slight rainfall. Based mainly upon these significant differences in both the amount and distribution of rainfall, two main tropical climatic types are recognized. They are: (1) Tropical Rainforest (Af) and (2) Tropical Savanna (Aw).

Tropical Rainforest (Af) The tropical rainforest type of climate has abundant rainfall with no month receiving less than 2.4 inches, and uniformly high temperatures throughout the year. It lies astride the equator and usually extends from 5° to 10° north and south latitude, except on the eastern side of continents where onshore trade winds yield abundant orographic rainfall along highland slopes as far as 20° or 25° from the equator.

Both monthly and annual temperatures average about 80°F. This is due to the fact that the angle of the sun's rays is continuously high and the length of day and night is always about equal. Diurnal or daily ranges of temperature are considerably greater than annual temperature ranges since day-time temperatures are commonly in the 90's while night-time temperatures frequently drop to the high

60's. It is commonly stated that "night is the winter of the tropics."

Areas of tropical rainforest are either under constant control of the equatorial low pressure area or in locations favorable for orographic rainfall effected by trade winds. Annual rainfall is well distributed because trade winds blow toward the equatorial low. As the air reaches it, an ascent takes place. Rising convectional air currents then cool adiabatically until the air is saturated with moisture. Vertically-developed clouds form which often bring thundershowers. Maximum daily rainfall occurs during the hottest time of the day when convectional updrafts are strongest. Annual rainfall amounts commonly vary from about 60 inches to more than 100 inches.

Uniformly heavy rainfall provides adequate and at times excessive moisture throughout the year. Water tables are always near the surface; frequently swamps and marshes occur in low-lying areas. Rivers are normally swollen by heavy run-off from frequent downpours.

The major land areas of the world having a tropical rainforest type of climate are: (1) the Amazon Basin of South America, (2) the Congo Basin of Africa,   (3) the east coast of Madagascar, and   (4) the mainland and islands of Southeast Asia. Singapore illustrates this type.

Singapore, Malaya. Lat. 1°14'N.; Long. 103°55'E.

	JAN.	FEB.	MAR.	APR.	MAY	JUNE	JULY	AUG.	SEPT.	OCT.	NOV.	DEC.	YEAR
T.	78.3	79.0	80.2	80.8	81.5	81.1	81.0	80.6	80.4	80.1	79.3	78.6	80.1
P.	8.5	6.1	6.5	6.9	7.2	6.7	6.8	8.5	7.1	8.2	10.0	10.4	92.9

In the Trewartha system of climatic classification, the *tropical monsoon* (*Am*) is considered a variation of the tropical rainforest. These climatic areas are characterized by a wet high-sun period caused by monsoonal indrafts and a dry low-sun period when the winds blow from land to sea. Temperatures are high with the average monthly maximums occurring just prior to the coming of the monsoon rains. Many weather stations record copious rains during the summer season and little or none during the winter. The major areas which have a monsoon type of climate are located in southern and southeastern Asia, along the Guinea coast of Africa, and in certain West Indian islands.

It should be noted that Singapore, Malaya, has relatively uniform temperature and precipitation. In contrast Calcutta, India, has a difference of more than 20° between the coldest month (January) and the warmest month (May). A distinct wet and dry season in Calcutta is caused by monsoon winds which blow into Asia from the Indian Ocean during the summer and from the continent to the sea during the winter season.

Calcutta, India. Lat. 22°32′N.; Long. 88°24′E.

	JAN.	FEB.	MAR.	APR.	MAY	JUNE	JULY	AUG.	SEPT.	OCT.	NOV.	DEC.	YEAR
T.	65.8	70.6	79.6	85.3	86.0	85.0	83.3	82.6	83.1	79.7	72.7	65.7	78.2
P.	0.4	1.1	1.4	2.1	5.3	11.5	12.4	12.5	9.5	4.6	0.5	0.2	61.5

TROPICAL SAVANNA (Aw) The tropical savannas are found poleward from tropical rainforests and from 5° to 15° from the equator. Tropical savanna areas have less precipitation than tropical rainforests, and precipitation is unevenly distributed in a marked wet and dry season. Shifting of the sun's vertical rays causes a distinct seasonal distribution of precipitation. The equatorial low pressure area, which always dominates the weather of tropical rainforests, moves into areas of tropical savanna only during the summer. During periods of low angle sun rays, trade winds prevail.

Average temperatures in tropical savanna climates are similar to those of tropical rainforests. Both the annual and diurnal ranges in temperature tend to be somewhat greater in tropical savannas because of greater changes in the angle at which the sun's rays strike the earth and increasing differences in the length of day and night. Highest temperatures generally precede the rainy season when overcast skies reduce insolation.

The outstanding feature of the tropical savanna climate is the marked seasonal contrast in precipitation. Annual precipitation is generally between 30 and 60 inches. Rainfall is less reliable than in tropical rainforests and the beginning of the rainy seasons is relatively unpredictable. The length of rainy seasons varies from five to eight months depending mainly upon proximity to the equator. As latitude increases, rainy periods shorten. During the wet summer season precipitation is usually at least ten times as much as during the dry winter season. Darwin, Australia, ranges from 15.3 inches in January to 0.1 during three winter months.

Darwin, Australia. Lat. 12°28'S.; Long. 130°51'E.

	JAN.	FEB.	MAR.	APR.	MAY	JUNE	JULY	AUG.	SEPT.	OCT.	NOV.	DEC.	YEAR
T.	84	83	84	84	82	79	77	79	83	85	86	85	83
P.	15.3	13.5	9.6	4.1	0.6	0.1	0.1	0.1	0.5	2.0	4.7	9.8	60.4

DRY CLIMATES (B)

Dry climates, that is, those in which evaporation exceeds precipitation, cover a greater percentage of the earth's surface than any other major climatic type. Dry climates occupy large areas in low latitudes from the interiors to the western coasts of continents. In middle latitudes, they are east of high mountains and far inland.

The aridity of a climate depends not only on the total precipitation but also upon the rate of evaporation. A dry climate is normally characterized by three features: (1) low precipitation amounts, (2) erratic distribution of precipitation, and (3) high evaporation rates. But in dry climates moisture evaporated exceeds precipitation.

DESERTS (BW) Most deserts are situated between 15° and 30° north and south latitudes respectively. They are areas of extreme temperature variations, low humidity, and limited rainfall. Violent convectional showers, which are limited both in extent and in number, sometimes occur, but skies are generally clear and sunshine abundant.

Regions between 15° and 30° are constantly under the influence of the trade winds or the subtropical high pressure zone. Trade wind air moving toward the equator is warmed and its capacity for holding moisture is increased. In consequence, evaporation rates are high. Air descending in the subtropical high pressure zone is warmed by compression and is, therefore, dry.

Some middle latitude deserts are the result of topographic barriers which prevent westerly winds from carrying moisture inland. Others are located so far inland that moisture-bearing air masses rarely penetrate the necessary distance. They differ from tropical deserts mainly by their colder temperature characteristics, but they are similar with respect to meager and unreliable rainfall.

Cairo, Egypt. Lat. 30°31'N.; Long. 31°15'E.

	JAN.	FEB.	MAR.	APR.	MAY	JUNE	JULY	AUG.	SEPT.	OCT.	NOV.	DEC.	YEAR
T.	55	57	63	70	76	80	82	82	78	74	65	58	70
P.	0.4	0.2	0.2	0.2	0	0	0	0	0	0	0.1	0.2	1.3

STEPPES (BS) Tropical steppes surround tropical deserts except on western sides of continents where deserts usually extend to oceans. They differ from tropical deserts mainly because of a short, but uncertain, wet season. During the wet season, the weather is similar to tropical savanna climates. The wet season, which extends from three to five months, occurs during the summer. During periods of low sun, very little rain occurs. Rainfall distribution at Monterrey, Mexico, characterizes the tropical steppe climate.

Monterrey, Mexico. Lat. 25°40'N.; Long. 100°18'W.

	JAN.	FEB.	MAR.	APR.	MAY	JUNE	JULY	AUG.	SEPT.	OCT.	NOV.	DEC.	YEAR
T.	58	62	68	73	79	82	82	83	78	71	64	57	71.4
P.	0.5	0.5	0.7	1.1	1.2	2.3	2.1	2.0	4.4	2.4	1.3	1.0	19.5

Middle latitude steppes are also transitional between dry and humid climates. Probably the most critical factor is unreliable precipitation. Annual rainfall averages are generally between 10 and 20 inches, but seasonal and annual variations are outstanding characteristics of this climatic type. Temperature and precipitation data for Denver, Colorado, typify middle latitude steppe climates.

Denver, Colorado. Lat. 39°41′N.; Long. 104°57′W.

	JAN.	FEB.	MAR.	APR.	MAY	JUNE	JULY	AUG.	SEPT.	OCT.	NOV.	DEC.	YEAR
T.	30	32	39	47	57	67	72	71	62	51	39	32	50
P.	0.4	0.5	1.0	2.1	2.4	1.4	1.8	1.4	1.0	1.0	0.6	0.7	14.3

WARM TEMPERATE CLIMATES (C)

Warm temperate climates are divided into three well-defined zones: (1) wet subtropical; (2) dry subtropical; and (3) west coast marine. Both the wet and dry subtropical climates are located in the vicinity of the equatorial parts of the mid-latitudes, while the west coast marine is located farther poleward.

The limits of these climates are relatively broad. They are considered to be generally middle latitude in location, but they occur from tropical latitudes to beyond 70° North and 50° South latitude. The warm temperate climates have seasons with heat and cold in response to the major air mass which dominates. The constant heat of the monotonous tropical climates is replaced by both erratic and seasonal weather changes.

WET SUBTROPICAL (Ca) Subtropical climates are located between 25° and 40° north latitude and south latitude, along both eastern and western coasts of continents. Eastern coasts are humid throughout the year in contrast with western coasts where summers are dry. Eastern coasts, from latitudes 25° to 40° (mostly 28° to 38°), are characterized by rainfall which totals from 30 to 65 inches annually. Maximum rainfall occurs during the spring and summer months. Winter, while not dry, is commonly less wet.

Summer temperatures are characteristically warm to hot. Monthly averages during summer are normally in the 70's and 80's, but daily maximum temperatures exceed humid tropical temperatures. Monthly averages during winter range in the 40's and 50's. Average annual temperatures normally range in the 50's or 60's. Residents find both the heat and cold penetrating because of generally high humidities. Diurnal ranges in temperatures are low because of high humidity and frequent cloudiness.

Wet subtropical climates are dominated by maritime tropical

air during the summer. The prevalence of warm ocean currents accentuates high humidities and increases summer precipitation. Winter precipitation is also dominantly frontal or cyclonic. Cool, rainy, overcast days are frequent in winter, but total precipitation is normally light. Nashville, Tennessee, has a typical weather record for a wet subtropical climate.

Nashville, Tennessee. Lat. 36°10'N.; Long. 86°46'W.

	JAN.	FEB.	MAR.	APR.	MAY	JUNE	JULY	AUG.	SEPT.	OCT.	NOV.	DEC.	YEAR
T.	39	41	50	59	68	76	79	78	72	69	49	41	59
P.	4.8	4.2	4.1	4.4	3.8	4.2	4.1	3.5	3.5	2.4	3.5	3.9	47.4

DRY SUBTROPICAL (Cs) Dry subtropical climates (Mediterranean) differ in three significant ways from wet subtropical climates: (1) less precipitation; (2) drier summers; and (3) locations on the western margins of continents. Dry subtropical climates are subhumid, with total annual precipitation generally between 15 and 25 inches. Most of the precipitation occurs during winter, since westerlies dominate and bring moisture in from adjacent oceans. During summer, subtropical high pressure cells shift poleward and dry winds dominate. Consequently, west coasts of continents from 30° to 40° receive little or no precipitation during summer.

The monthly average temperatures during winter range between the 40's and 50's; summer temperatures between the 70's and 80's. High daytime temperatures occur during summer months and occasional freezing temperatures occur during the short winter season. Because summers are dry, clear weather is the rule. Sunshine is relatively abundant even during the winter rainy season.

Los Angeles, California. Lat. 34°3'N.; Long. 118°15'W.

	JAN.	FEB.	MAR.	APR.	MAY	JUNE	JULY	AUG.	SEPT.	OCT.	NOV.	DEC.	YEAR
T.	54.5	55.5	57.3	59.7	62.1	65.2	70.2	71.1	69.4	65.1	60.9	55.3	62.2
P.	3.3	3.2	2.9	0.9	0.4	0.1	0.0	0.0	0.2	0.7	1.2	2.7	15.6

WEST COAST MARINE (CB, Cc) Typically west coast marine climates occur poleward of 40° on the west side of continents. Relatively cool summers and mild winters are common. Monthly average temperatures during winter are in the 40's and 50's, and summer monthly average temperatures are usually in the 50's and 60's. Annual monthly and daily temperature variations are moderate. These temperature conditions cause the west coast marine climate to be truly a "temperate" climate with average annual temperatures normally from 45°F. to 55°F.

Moderate precipitation occurs throughout the year, but winter rains are much heavier than those of summer. Cyclonic storms, which are made up of maritime polar air masses brought inland by westerly winds, cause frequent periods of rainy weather. In some areas, cyclonic precipitation is augmented by orographic effects. During winter, light showers, gentle drizzles, cloudy and foggy weather are common. In summer, sunny days are more frequent and rainfall is lighter. There is a wide range of annual precipitation in the west coast marine climate with variations from 20 inches to over 100 inches on windward slopes of mountains.

Seattle, Washington. Lat. 47°45′N.; Long. 122°25′W.

	JAN.	FEB.	MAR.	APR.	MAY	JUNE	JULY	AUG.	SEPT.	OCT.	NOV.	DEC.	YEAR
T.	40	42	45	50	55	60	64	64	59	52	46	42	51.4
P.	4.9	3.8	3.1	2.4	1.8	1.3	0.6	0.7	1.7	2.8	4.8	5.5	33.4

COOL TEMPERATE CLIMATES (D)

Cool temperate climates are characteristic of large land areas in North America and Eurasia. They have lower temperatures, shorter growing seasons, and greater temperature ranges than warm temperate climates. Cold temperate climates are located only in the interior and eastern coasts of the higher middle latitudes in the northern hemisphere. They are predominantly controlled by large land masses and the interaction of contrasting air masses. Two types are recognized, namely, humid continental and subarctic.

HUMID CONTINENTAL (DA, DB) Humid continental climates are found between 38° and 60° north latitude in interior and eastern coasts of North America and Eurasia. With the pronounced effects of air masses, fronts, and cyclonic storms over continents within the westerly wind belt, the humid continental climate is more rigorous than climates of similar latitudes on west coasts. Nevertheless, the humid continental climate region is more densely populated and more intensely utilized in North America.

Temperatures are highly variable both seasonally and diurnally. Solar insolation exceeds that of the tropics during summer, since daylight is longer. On the other hand, winter temperatures are low because of low sun angles and short daylight periods. Importations of contrasting temperatures by air masses from polar or tropical sources frequently bring sharp daily temperature changes. Winter temperatures average in the 20's and 30's with at least one month below freezing. Fewer than six months are below 32°F., and at least three months are above 50°F.

Precipitation is also variable, but, in general, it decreases both in amount and reliability from the humid margins toward continental interiors, and in the direction of higher latitudes. Maximum rainfall usually occurs during summer, although it is often fairly well-distributed throughout the year. Some summer rainfall is convectional, but most of it is frontal or cyclonic. Since the westerlies are characterized by a sequence of high and low pressure cells, cyclonic or frontal precipitation is observed at all seasons. Consequently, the combined convectional and cyclonic sources yield greater precipitation during summer than cyclonic sources yield alone during winter. Precipitation is fairly evenly distributed throughout the year as shown by the climatic data below for Chicago, Illinois.

Chicago, Illinois. Lat. 41°53′N.; Long. 87°38′W.

	JAN.	FEB.	MAR.	APR.	MAY	JUNE	JULY	AUG.	SEPT.	OCT.	NOV.	DEC.	YEAR
T.	26	27	37	47	58	68	74	73	66	55	42	30	50
P.	2.1	2.1	2.6	2.9	3.6	3.3	3.4	3.0	3.1	2.6	2.4	2.1	33.2

SUBARCTIC (Dc, Dd) Subarctic (subpolar) climates are located between about 50° and 65° north latitude. Temperatures at their northern limits are so severe that only one month has an average temperature of about 50°F. (coincides with tree growth limits) while six or more months have temperatures below freezing. Southern limits border on humid continental or middle latitude steppe climates. Long, bitterly cold winters with very short summers are the rule. To compensate somewhat for the short summers are very long periods of daylight and very short periods of night. Summer maximum temperatures frequently rise above 80°F. Subarctic climates have the widest seasonal temperature ranges of all climates. Ranges of 120°F. to 150°F. are common in many areas. Perhaps the lowest subarctic temperatures have been recorded in Siberia where, at Oimekon, an unofficial —108°F. was recorded. In North America the lowest subarctic temperature was officially reported as —81°F.

Subarctic regions generally have from 10 to 20 inches of precipitation annually. It is mostly of cyclonic origin. Polar easterlies blow from cold polar regions, and produce a little precipitation. A summer maximum occurs during the season of peak heating. Winter snows actually account for only a small part of the total precipitation. Climatic data for Dawson, Alaska, support these statements.

Dawson, Alaska. Lat. 64°3'N.; Long. 139°25'W.

	JAN.	FEB.	MAR.	APR.	MAY	JUNE	JULY	AUG.	SEPT.	OCT.	NOV.	DEC.	YEAR
T.	—23	—11	4	29	46	57	59	54	42	25	1	—13	23
P.	0.8	0.8	0.5	0.7	0.9	1.3	1.6	1.6	1.7	1.3	1.3	1.1	13.6

POLAR CLIMATES (E)

Polar climates are the least extensive of all major climatic types. They have several outstandingly adverse characteristics among which are long continued and monotonous cold winters without any warm season. This is a most adverse factor in affecting development. In addition, the areas have little available moisture due to limited precipitation and extended periods of subfreezing temperatures. Two types are recognized within the polar climates, namely, *tundra* and *polar ice cap*. They are commonly located at high latitudes over both land and water bodies.

TUNDRA (ET) Tundra climates are associated with continental polar and continental arctic air masses. They border the Arctic coast of North America and Eurasia and lie north of subarctic climates. Average temperatures of the warmest month are between 32°F. and 50°F. Mean annual temperatures are usually below freezing. Barrow, Alaska, for example, has an annual mean of 10°F., but the January average is —19°F. The annual range of 59°F. between January and July indicates a distinct continental characteristic of Barrow's climate despite its coastal location.

The tundra climates are normally characterized by less than 10 inches of annual precipitation. Neither the low summer temperatures nor winter high pressure areas from Arctic air masses are conducive to precipitation. Precipitation normally falls during the summer months and is principally cyclonic or frontal in origin. Meager falls of dry powdery snow are normal for the winter, and occasional falls are not unusual during the summer.

Barrow, Alaska. Lat. 71°23′N.; Long. 156°30′W.

	JAN.	FEB.	MAR.	APR.	MAY	JUNE	JULY	AUG.	SEPT.	OCT.	NOV.	DEC.	YEAR
T.	—19	—13	—14	—2	21	35	40	39	31	16	0	—15	10
P.	0.3	0.2	0.2	0.3	0.3	0.3	1.1	0.8	0.5	0.8	0.4	0.4	5.6

POLAR ICE CAP (EF) Polar ice cap climates are found only in Greenland and Antarctica. No month has an average temperature above 32°F., consequently, a permanent cover of ice and snow accumulates. The lowest official recorded temperature has been observed in Antarctica, —102.1°F., but it is probable that some winter temperatures are even lower. At any rate, continuously low temperatures preclude permanent human settlement.

Little America, Antarctica. Lat. 78°34′S.; Long. 163°56′W.

	JAN.	FEB.	MAR.	APR.	MAY	JUNE	JULY	AUG.	SEPT.	OCT.	NOV.	DEC.	YEAR
T.	22	9	—7	—24	—27	—29	—34	—34	—29	—14	8.6	24	—13.3
P.	No data.												

UNDIFFERENTIATED HIGHLANDS (H)

The outstanding feature of undifferentiated highlands is diversity. Almost a limitless variety of climates is found on the world's highlands. Altitude and topography are the principal climatic controls, and temperatures and precipitations are both erratic. Precipitation is commonly orographic in origin, and temperatures are normally characterized by great diurnal contrasts.

STUDY QUESTIONS

1. Why does heavy rainfall occur throughout the year in the tropical rainforest?
2. Explain what is meant by the statement "night is the winter of the tropics."
3. Explain the geographic reasons for the wet and dry seasons of the tropical savanna.
4. Why are summers dry in the dry subtropical climates?
5. Why are most deserts located between 15° and 30° north and south latitude?
6. Why are the average annual ranges of temperature high in subarctic climates?
7. What factors contribute to aridity?
8. Name the temperature and precipitation characteristics of:
   (a) tropical rainforest   (d) low latitude steppe
   (b) dry subtropical   (e) subarctic
   (c) west coast marine   (f) tundra

SELECTED REFERENCES

Finch, V. C., Trewartha, G. T., Robinson, A. H. and Hammond, E. H. *Elements of Geography* (New York: McGraw-Hill Book Co., Inc., 4th Edition, 1957), pp. 128-206.

James, P. E. (Kline, H. V. B., Jr., Collaborator). *A Geography of Man* (New York: Ginn and Company, 1949).

Thornthwaite, C. W. "The Climates of the Earth," *Geographical Review,* vol. 23, 1933, pp. 433-440.

Ward, H. B. and Powers, W. E. *An Introduction to the Study of Weather and Climate* (Evanston: Northwestern University), pp. 85-107.

Ward, R. DeC. *Climate* (New York: G. P. Putnam's Sons, 1908).

White, C. L. and Renner, G. T. *College Geography* (New York: Appleton-Century-Crofts, Inc., 1957), pp. 51-291.

Chapter Seven

LANDFORMS

Landforms, like weather elements and climates, are phenomena to which man shows great sensitivity. Similarly, landforms affect climates, drainage, vegetation, and soils. All landforms are transitory features. They are in a constant state of flux. A never ending struggle goes on between constructive forces which are attempting to build up the surface of the land and those destructive forces which are wearing it down. High mountains, deep valleys, and ocean basins are comparatively less significant on the face of the earth than wrinkles on the face of a man. Nothing is constant in landforms but change.

THE EARTH'S CRUST (LITHOSPHERE)

Rocks are the main materials composing the earth's crust. There are many different kinds of rocks, but they can be classified, according to origin, into *igneous, sedimentary,* and *metamorphic.* Rocks are composed of minerals. *Minerals* are natural inorganic substances each with a fairly definite chemical composition and recognizable *crystal form, color, hardness, luster, fracture,* and other physical characteristics.

IGNEOUS ROCKS Rocks which have solidified directly from molten materials are called igneous rocks. To a certain extent, all other rocks originate from igneous rocks; therefore, igneous rocks are commonly referred to as primary rocks. Igneous rocks compose the greater part of the earth's crust, but they are generally covered at the surface by a relatively thin layer of sedimentary or metamorphic rocks.

Igneous rocks are distinguished by the following characteristics: (1) they contain no fossils; (2) they usually show a distinctly uniform appearance; (3) they are not layered; and (4) they are nearly always made up of crystals.

Igneous rocks may be *intrusive* (solidified beneath the surface) or *extrusive* (solidified at the surface) in origin. Because they cool more slowly intrusive rocks show a better developed crystalline structure and crystals are larger than those rocks which have cooled at the surface. Some common intrusive rocks are granite, diorite, gabbro, peridotite, and diabase. Extrusive rocks of significance include: obsidian (volcanic glass), rhyolite (the extrusive equivalent of granite), andesite (which corresponds to diorite), and basalt (the extrusive version of diabase). Certain lavas contain small gaseous pockets, which, when they escape produce a porous material such as scoria or pumice.

SEDIMENTARY ROCKS Sedimentary rocks are composed of fragments of existing rocks or they may be of organic or chemical origin. *Clastic* rocks are those which are formed when weathered products of existing rocks are cemented together to form a new rock. There tend to be distinct layers of such sediments as gravels, sand, and clay as they are deposited by water and occasionally wind. They vary with the material and the power of the eroding agent. The materials are deposited in a manner to form layers, a common characteristic of sedimentary rock.

When clastic sediments harden into sedimentary rocks, the names applied to them change, to indicate the change in physical state. Thus, cemented gravel, cobbles, or boulders become *conglomerate;* cemented sand becomes *sandstone;* and hardened mud becomes *shale.* The principal distinction between these clastic sedimentary rocks is one of varying particle size. Other sedimentary rocks, such as limestone, result from the deposition of dissolved material. The ingredient parts are normally precipitated by organic substances, or are the consequence of the accumulation of shells of clams or hard skeletons of other marine life, coral, algae, etc. Dolomite is similar to limestone, but it is composed of calcium-magnesium carbonate instead of calcium carbonate. Coal is composed of the remains of luxurious swamp vegetation of past geologic time.

Certain chemical sediments, called evaporites, have evolved

in enclosed water bodies where evaporation is especially rapid. Rocks of this class include: halite (rock salt), anhydrite, and gypsum.

METAMORPHIC ROCKS Both igneous and sedimentary rocks may be changed by pressure, heat, solution, or cementing action. When individual grains tend to deform and interlock from existing rocks, they are then called metamorphic rocks. For example, granite, an igneous rock, may be metamorphosed into a gneiss. Limestone, a sedimentary rock, may become marble. Sandstone may be metamorphosed into quartzite, and shale; when greatly compressed, into slate.

Most igneous, sedimentary, and metamorphic rocks are buried beneath broken-up materials called mantle rock. The rate of weathering of rocks is contingent upon the rock type exposed and weathering agents. At the upper part of the mantle rock is usually a soil zone which contains micro-organisms, plant roots, and other life forms. It is from this zone that all plant life develops.

THE EARTH'S INTERIOR

Since our deepest wells go only about four miles below the earth's surface, knowledge of the earth's interior must be gained by indirect methods. From the study of the behavior of earthquake waves, and from the earth's gravitational relationships, much has been determined about the earth's interior.

Deep mines and wells show gradual increases in temperature with depth. Rates of increase vary from about 1 degree F. per 60 feet to about 1 degree F. per 100 feet. This temperature gradient is doubtless greater near the surface than at greater depths for if it continued for 4,000 miles to the center of the earth, a temperature of several hundred thousand degrees would result. It is generally believed that there is a significant source of heat in the earth from radioactivity of rocks at depths of about 25 to 30 miles. Very little heat is being conducted from the deep interior to the radioactive zone. Practically no temperature increases occur with depths below the radioactive zone.

Rocks at 30 miles depth have a temperature of about 2,000 degrees F., which is above the melting point of ordinary rocks at the earth's surface. However, the melting points of rocks are higher within the earth because pressures are greater, since they support the weight of overlying materials.

Volcanoes are evidence of a fluid pocket of rock material; however, if any considerable part of the earth were in a liquid state, enormous bulges would be raised on the earth's surface as a result of the attraction of the sun and the moon. Actually a deformation of a few inches does occur, but this is no greater than would take place in a globe of steel the size of the earth. Rock in the earth's interior sometimes becomes molten when the enormous pressure over it is suddenly released.

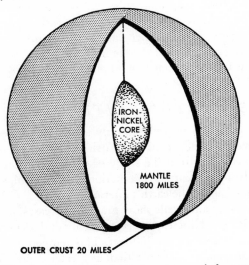

Fig. 9   Presumed physical structure of the earth

A general profile of the zones in the earth's interior includes: (1) A 10 to 20 mile outer crust which is composed chiefly of light crystalline rocks.   (2) A zone of mantle rock below the crust which continues to a depth of about 1,800 miles.   (3) A heavy, dark iron-nickel core below a depth of about 1,800 miles and extending to the center of the earth. This last zone is thought to be solid very near to the center of the earth and possibly fluid above.

SHAPING OF LANDFORMS

The processes of *volcanism* and *diastrophism* yield landforms. These forces may be sudden and cataclysmic or so gradual they pass unnoticed for long periods of time.

VOLCANISM Volcanic action is a spectacular type of constructive force which alters landforms. Volcanoes originate from depths where temperatures are higher than the melting point of rocks. From these areas, molten rock sometimes works its way to the earth's surface and flows out over land through a zone of crustal weakness.

When intense pressures are built up, liquid rock or magma bubbles quietly or bursts out violently. The manner of eruption depends mainly upon how much gas pressure is present and how tight the plug is in the volcano's neck. For example, a volcano named Krakatoa, blew to bits an entire island in Indonesia in 1883. Great waves were encountered throughout the Pacific Ocean, its eruption was heard 3,000 miles away, and volcanic dust from this explosion circulated throughout the earth's atmosphere for many years. In contrast, Mauna Loa in Hawaii, continuously discharges highly fluid lava in a quiet non-explosive manner. Each volcano has its individual characteristics. Some, such as Vesuvius in Italy, have a relatively regular period of eruption. Others, such as Stromboli, have weak eruptions almost continuously.

The earth's great volcano belt borders the Pacific Ocean, known as the "ring of fire," from South America to Alaska, from Alaska to Japan, and southward to Indonesia. A smaller belt extends westward through Mediterranean Europe, the Canary Islands, and the West Indies to Central America. About 90 per cent of all volcanoes are concentrated along coastlines, and most volcanoes are located in young, rugged mountain chains.

Edges of continents mark sharp changes in the structure of the earth's crust. Volcanoes are most likely to occur along zones of weakness in the earth's crust, through which molten rock can work its way to the surface. Magma finds easiest release along these belts of weakness.

DIASTROPHISM There are three main types of diastrophic actions. They are: (1) *warping*, (2) *folding*, and (3) *fracturing*. As the earth's surface is slowly bent, it gradually bulges upward or downward over a large area. This is called *warping*. Large areas of the earth's surface are often slowly squeezed together, resulting in *folding* of rock layers alternately upward and downward. The upward folds are called *anticlines* and the downward folds are called *synclines*. When intense force is exerted on the earth's crust, *fractures* may develop. Some fractures are relatively unimportant, but others are large enough to be of major significance.

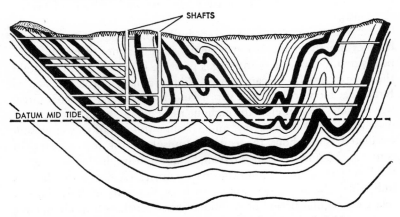

Fig. 10   Folded structures in the anthracite coal fields of the United States

A fracture is called a *joint* if no movement occurs along the break; however, if appreciable movement takes place then the fracture is known as a fault. If the movement is downward, it is known as a *normal fault;* if the movement is upward, it is a *thrust fault;* and if the movement is sidewise, it is a *horizontal fault*. A block which is thrust up between two essentially parallel fault lines is known as a *horst,* whereas a down-dropped block between such faults is known as a *graben,* or *rift valley*. A vast system of such rift valleys is present in the lake district of east Africa, through Ethiopia, into the Red Sea, and into the Dead Sea—Jordan Valley trench of Israel and Jordan. Faulting is the principal cause of

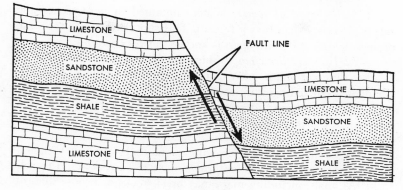

Fig. 11 A normal fault

earthquakes, or vibratory tremors set up by the frictional resistance between two opposite masses of rock moving along a fault plane.

More than 1,000 earthquakes occur daily. The earth's vibratory motions range from light tremors to extreme shock. Sometimes a mass of rock is bent by powerful forces and suddenly slips like a released spring. Some areas are gradually tilted upward, or are dropped downward very slowly. Slow changes of this type are imperceptible to us, but in time they also have far-reaching effects upon man.

DESTRUCTIVE FORCES Irregularities created by constructive forces uplifting landforms usually accelerate the action of destructive forces because they operate steadily to level the earth's surface again. Any landform above sea level is constantly graded by destructive agents of weathering and erosion.

WEATHERING Weathering is the process of altering rocks at or near the earth's surface. Two distinct types are (1) mechanical (disintegration) and (2) chemical (decomposition).

Disintegration is the mechanical breaking down of rocks into smaller fragments thus changing their physical character. Smaller pieces of the same material are created without chemical change or alteration.

A number of surface processes disintegrate rock, the more important of which are:

1. *Freezing of water.* Water contained in pore spaces and cracks of rocks expands as it freezes. This rupturing of the rock and prying the mineral grains apart is known as *frost wedging*.

2. *Temperature changes.* Heat tends to disrupt rocks because of the different rates of expansion of rock-building minerals. Changes in air temperature cause the cracking of minerals in outer surfaces of rocks and aid rocks to scale or flake off at the surface. This process of flaking or stripping off of small plates of rock from a larger rock mass is called *exfoliation*.

3. *Organic activity.* Growing plant roots can pry rock materials loose, and plants which grow in cracks of rocks tend to split rocks. Animals, including man, may break rocks or expose them to the activity of other weathering agents. Man aids in breaking up rocks by quarrying, blasting, roadbuilding, bombing, and other activities while the burrowing activities of animals loosen easily-excavated materials.

Other disintegration processes. Solid rock masses may be broken apart mechanically by: (a) the removal of grains in rocks by rainfall; (b) wedging apart of rock by water driven into cracks by waves along the coast; (c) shattering during volcanic eruptions; (d) shattering of fragments loosened from cliffs or along slopes when they fall with the pull of gravity; and (e) wind blowing dust and sand against rocks.

Decomposition is the chemical decay of rock materials. Original minerals are changed to form new substances, some of which may be dissolved and carried downward or away in solution. The chemical alteration of the minerals in surface rocks is directly or indirectly the result of atmospheric effects. The principal decomposition agents are oxygen, carbon dioxide, and water vapor.

1. *Oxidation.* The combining of oxygen with another substance containing oxidizable elements produces compounds known as oxides. Iron in rocks combines with oxygen to form hematite, or it may combine with oxygen and water to form limonite. Rusty stains on weathered rocks and yellow to dark brown colors of many rocks and soils are mixtures of hematite and limonite.

2. *Carbonation.* Carbon dioxide dissolved in water forms carbonic acid which slowly attacks many minerals to form car-

bonates and aids, in turn, in dissolving them. Thus, the combining of carbon dioxide with any part of a mineral produces compounds known as carbonates.

3. *Hydration.* The combining of any part of a mineral with water produces hydrous compounds, and water alone slowly attacks many minerals to form hydrated products from the original compounds. These materials are normally less resistant than the substances from which they were derived.

4. *Solution.* Carbon dioxide in the atmosphere is absorbed by raindrops to form weak carbonic acid. As the rain sinks into the soil and percolates through the bedrock, it dissolves soluble products formed by other types of weathering. Acids produced by plants and animals also aid in making ground water a potent agent of solution.

These processes of weathering are widespread and generally occur together. They are all present in variable form and frequency everywhere over the earth's surface at all times. Low temperatures and aridity decrease the rate of weathering, whereas high temperatures and heavy rainfall greatly increase it. Generally, in regions with rainy tropical climates the rate of weathering is rapid and in middle latitude deserts relatively slow.

Erosion Several agents are continuously active in grading the earth's surface. These erosional forces gradually wear down the land, and materials removed are deposited as sediment on ocean floors or in land depressions. Four principal agents which erode land surfaces are *running water, moving ice, wind,* and *waves.*

Stream erosion is the most widespread of all those erosional agents. It transports weathered and loose material from land surfaces and grinds away rock masses by abrasion. The removal of parts of the earth's surface by running water develops stream valleys which are continually lengthened, deepened, and widened.

Like all natural processes, stream erosion operates in an orderly fashion in obedience to controlling principles called natural laws. The successive stages of stream erosion may be identified by observing certain physical characteristics of the stream and associated areas.

The first water to drain from newly exposed surfaces will fol-

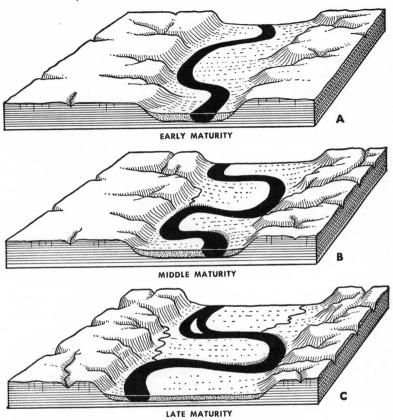

EARLY MATURITY

MIDDLE MATURITY

LATE MATURITY

Fig. 12   A stream and its valley in various stages of maturity

low any initial slope. There may be few if any initial valleys. The first erosive action will be largely down-cutting to form gullies which will later become widened. Original valleys and stream patterns have the following youthful characteristics: (1) a small number of main streams along with a few large tributaries, but with many gullies, developing headward;   (2) narrow and gorge-like stream valleys usually comparatively deep;   (3) a general absence of flood-plains, and valley walls rising usually directly from the water's edge; (4) regions between stream valleys almost undissected and often poorly drained; (5) abundant waterfalls and rapids; and (6) the stream course comparatively straight.

As streams continue to erode, their valleys are deepened, widened, and their slopes reduced. Land surfaces become more dissected by valleys and narrow, sharp divides separate one stream from another. Because of decreased velocities, the streams become loaded with sediment. Downcutting ceases but lateral erosion still continues thus starting flat valley bottoms commonly called flood plains. When these changes occur streams assume the following general characteristics of maturity: (1) many main streams with many tributaries; (2) broader valleys with more gently sloping walls; (3) limited development of flood plains taking place in the major river; (4) divides between streams heavily dissected giving minimum area between streams; (5) no water-falls, lakes, or marshes; and (6) streams begin to develop a meandering course.

Maturing usually continues for long intervals of time during which the flood plains are steadily widened. The gradients of the streams are gradually decreased and the divides are progressively worn down. The number of tributaries is decreased by the uniting of valley bottoms and the elimination of divides. Thus, the stream valleys have the following features which characterize regions of old age: (1) there are comparatively fewer main streams, but these are of larger size. The number of tributaries is less than in maturity, but more than in youth; (2) valleys are extremely broad and gently sloping laterally; (3) marked development of flood plains occurs as the stream flows in a meandering course; (4) areas between streams have been reduced to minimum size; (5) no water-falls remain although marshes may be present due to a high water table in swampy areas; (6) ox-bow lakes have developed, and there is a pronounced meandering of streams.

In classifying stream stages recognition is given to the fact that the transition from one stage to another is gradual. The analogy between the life history of a stream and that of a person is valid. No single birthday can mark the change from youth to maturity; adolescence is a long period of time in the aging of a stream. It is often desirable to subdivide stream stages by using terms as late youth, or early maturity, and normally in a river system the tributaries are younger than the streams into which they flow. If the lower stream reaches late maturity, the portion midway upstream is in early maturity, and nearer its head youthful characteristics are found.

STREAM PATTERNS Because of topographic and structural conditions streams and their tributaries develop characteristic patterns. A *dendritic* pattern looks much like the trunk and branches of a tree with tributaries entering the main stream and larger tributaries at acute angles upstream. *Radial patterns* develop when water flows down a symmetrical slope, such as a volcano, in a radiating pattern similar to the spokes of a wheel. Sedimentary domes frequently erode so that the streams assume a concentric ring-like appearance known as an *annular* pattern. Ridges and valleys, arranged in echelon, develop tributaries that enter main streams almost at right angles. Such an arrangement is known as a *trellis* pattern. A similar pattern of right angle tributaries evolves in areas of faulted or jointed rock. This type of system is called a *rectangular* pattern. In semiarid lands streams which are choked with debris develop a series of small branches within a large bed. The same kind of pattern may form on flood plains if excessive water is a common occurrence. This type pattern is termed *braided*. *Centripetal* drainage results when water flows into a basin from the surrounding sides. *Glacially deranged* drainage, with an odd helter skelter pattern, results from the unequal distribution of glacial drift.

Ice erosion occurs in areas of cold climates. Where there is abundant precipitation, winter snow may accumulate and gradually change to ice by partial melting under pressure and cause ice erosion. Ice of this origin forms in upper portions of valleys in mountainous areas and in polar ice cap climates. When ice accumulations become large they move down valleys as glaciers and cause rapid erosion. Glaciers, as powerful erosional agents, leave many scours upon the earth's surface.

The rate of movement of a glacier depends upon its gradient, thickness, and temperature. Some glaciers flow down to oceans, where they break off and form icebergs. However, most glaciers lose their ice by sublimation and by melting. Rock fragments plucked by moving ice generally litter the surface definitely near the lower end of a glacier.

Ice-scour features of mountain and valley glaciers frequently add to the ruggedness of mountain regions. Vast amphitheater-like basins carved by glacial ice near its source in mountains are called *cirques*. Jagged ridges which are produced by ice moving down opposite sides of a mountain ridge are termed *arêtes*. Where ice has cut through a ridge producing a saddle or notch, the feature is called a *col*. A *horn* (sometimes termed *Matterhorn*) is a glacially scoured peak.

Rock fragments frozen in the base and sides of glaciers carve valley bottoms and sides into troughs with deep U-shaped profiles. When glaciers have melted, the valleys will have transformed into deep troughs whose floors have reverse slopes which hold water back and form lakes. When such a lake occupies a portion of the floor of a cirque it is known as a *tarn*. Tributary glaciers may not be so effective at ice scour as the main ice stream and when these tributary glaciers have retreated some troughs may stand at an elevation above the principal trough. Such features are known as *hanging valleys* or *hanging troughs*. Glacially scoured valleys subsequently drowned by the sea produce long narrow embayments known as *fiords*.

Glaciers cover about 10 per cent (nearly 6,000,000 square miles) of the land area of the earth, although in past geologic time they were much more extensive. Vast ice sheets of Antarctica account for about 86 per cent of the world's ice area, and the Greenland ice cap makes up another 10 per cent. The remaining 4 per cent of the world's glaciers are mostly in mountainous areas. Estimates of the total volume of water in the world's glaciers are such that if all this ice melted, the level of the oceans would rise by as much as 200 feet.

Continental ice sheets can only accumulate in areas where annual snowfalls are enough to exceed annual melting. Consequently, ice sheets are not necessarily thickest where climates are coldest. Many areas in the coldest parts of the Arctic are barren of glaciers because there is not enough snowfall.

A number of theories have been promulgated concerning the

accumulation of continental glaciers during the last great ice age. For many years it was assumed that diminished insolation produced a colder climate permitting accumulation of snow, which was ultimately compacted into glacial ice. Certain theorists now suggest that an open Arctic Ocean, created either by temperature increases or warming by ocean currents, supplied a source of moisture which greatly increased snowfall and resulted in ice accumulation.

Whatever the cause, ice accumulated in great centers, and at least four such centers served as foci from which ice moved over much of North America. Similar centers of ice accumulation and movement are recognized for Europe and Asia. During the Pleistocene (last great ice age) there appears to have been four major advances and retreats of the ice. Interglacial periods were usually sufficiently lengthy to allow for the establishment of a vegetative mantle over glaciated terrain. Continental ice retreated from the United States about 10,000 years ago, but certain sections of dead ice were still present in Scandinavia as recently as 5,000 years ago.

Earlier geological periods experienced glaciation, which was continental in scope, but subsequent developments have obliterated all but the most obvious of their influences. The pendulum swing of earth history suggests that we are in an interglacial period and that future continental glaciation is likely.

Vast accumulations of glacial ice, such as polar ice caps, cover hills and valleys alike. They are pushed outward by thicker ice in the center and slowly move over land surfaces toward the edges. These continental ice sheets obey the same dynamic regulations as valley glaciers. The differences between shaping of landforms of the two types of glaciers are caused by differences in extent. Ice sheets are not confined between valley walls but spread out over large areas; consequently erosion by continental ice sheets is generally less vigorous than valley glaciers. Some of the common ice scour features include ice scour plains where glacial ice has removed top soil and mantle rock and modified pre-existent landforms.

Smaller ice scour features include *glacial grooves* and *glacial striae,* which are large and small scratches, respectively, made by rock particles imbedded in the ice passing over bedrock. *Roches moutonnées* are small, asymmetrically scoured portions of bedrock, which look to the imaginative observer like grazing sheep.

Wind erosion is limited to land surfaces which are dry and unprotected by vegetative cover, such as deserts, or dry barren farm land. Due to turbulence of air, finer dust particles may be picked up by wind and carried for hundreds of miles. Sand and coarser particles which are eroded bounce along on the ground and are usually not transported such great distances.

Winds annually erode an enormous amount of material. Although effects of wind-work are most conspicuous in regions of aridity and scanty vegetation, their consequences are noticeable even in humid regions where surface materials are exposed, as along beaches and river flats.

The removal of particles by the wind, called *deflation,* may produce some interesting landform features. When finer particles are removed by deflation and larger rocks and pebbles are left behind the resultant surface is known as a *desert pavement* or a *reg.* Abrasion by sand particles transported by the wind may modify existing land forms into bizarre shapes.

Wave erosion results from wind blown waters and shore currents which wear away the rocks and soils of the coasts which they contact. When waves reach shallow water adjacent to the shore, they break and their water flows as currents either along the shore, or along the bottom toward deeper water as an undertow. Eroded rock fragments are washed from shore by waves and are ground into sand and silt. These products are distributed by currents and undertow.

As waves attack promontories projecting into the sea the effect is to truncate the headland producing cliffs. Subsequent erosion may undermine portions of a headland producing a *sea arch.* When only resistant portions of the original headland are left standing detached offshore, such features are known as *stacks.* Material eroded from projecting headlands may be used as tools in eroding a step-like platform, which is known as a *wave-cut terrace.*

Coast lines vary, depending upon the nature of the shore on which erosion processes are operating, and on the stage of development. Two fundamental types of shorelines are commonly recognized: (1) irregular shorelines of submergence, and (2) regular shorelines of emergence. Submerging shorelines have an irregular profile with deep bays which were formerly stream valleys. These deep and irregular shore characteristics help to promote navigation. Emerging shorelines normally have a smooth, slightly dipping plane into the sea without indentations. These regular, shallow shore characteristics generally prohibit all but small-scale navigation. Because of the agencies of weathering and erosion, shorelines of whatever type tend to become more regular as the old age stage of the erosion cycle approaches.

DEPOSITION OF LANDFORMS

Most of the material transported by agents of erosion is deposited as some form of sediment. Sediments deposited on land are usually spread out in areas such as stream valleys, lakes, or stream beds. Each erosive agent, when depositing sediment, develops characteristics which serve to identify the manner of deposition and the erosional agent which brought it.

Stream Deposits Stream deposits are composed of pebbles, gravels, sand, silts, and clays. However, the size of the material tends to be approximately the same in any vicinity. It is well sorted, which shows the selective effect of the stream that carried and deposited it. Valley flats show better sorting and more stratification than areas with a steeper gradient.

Streams deposit part, or all, of their load wherever their carrying power may be decreased below that necessary to carry the sediment. Carrying power may be decreased by changing the shape of the stream channel so as to increase friction with the stream bed. Velocity is most commonly reduced by a decrease in the stream gradient, or when a stream flows into a body of standing water.

In consequence of these and other factors, stream deposits are found as *alluvial fans* at the foot of slopes or as *deltas* at places where streams enter ponds, lakes, or seas. When a swift stream flows down from high areas to a nearly level area, the abrupt change in its gradient may cause it to block its own channel and subsequently pile up its sediments to form conical mounds. In this way, an alluvial fan is built up. As the current at the mouth of a stream carrying excessive sediments is abruptly slowed down by standing

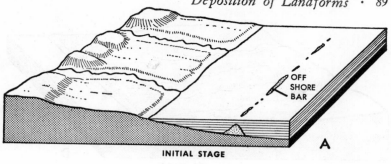

INITIAL STAGE **A**

OFF SHORE BAR

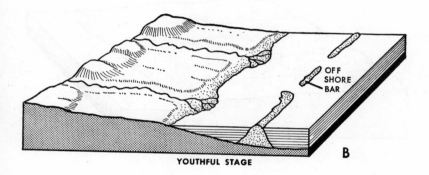

YOUTHFUL STAGE **B**

OFF SHORE BAR

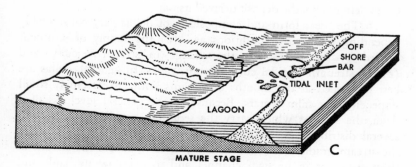

MATURE STAGE **C**

OFF SHORE BAR

TIDAL INLET

LAGOON

Fig. 13. A shoreline of emergence and its sequential development

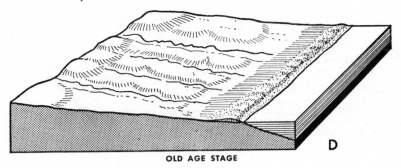

OLD AGE STAGE

D

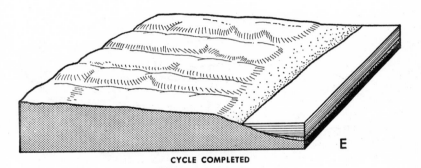

CYCLE COMPLETED

E

water, the load is dropped. As the fill is built up, deposits make a triangular-shaped area of new land. From the resemblance of the Greek letter delta, the deposit derived its name.

The exact form and composition of deltas vary considerably depending upon such conditions as: (a) the supply of sediment carried by the river, (b) the change in stream velocity, and (c) the strength of tidal currents and waves. In general, deltas are best developed at the mouths of streams with an extremely small slope entering calm waters. Because of the general levelness of a delta, the streams which carry the sediment usually flow through several distributaries. As the distributary channels are lengthened, the stream gradient is reduced. This, in turn, causes the stream to drop sediment in its own channel and to overflow its bank and deposit sediments on the delta surface. As overflowing is repeated, the relief of the delta is lessened. Occasionally, the gradient becomes so slight and the river bed becomes so high that the river abandons its old course to find a newer and lower channel.

GLACIAL DEPOSITS Ice deposits display a much wider variation in size and a much more irregular distribution than any other erosional agent. Glacial deposits involving direct ice action are unstratified, unsorted mixtures of sediments. Glacial sediments commonly rest on grooved surfaces, but they may be carried far beyond the outer ice margin by water.

Till plains result from continental glaciation which cover relatively large areas with unstratified sediments. Because of their nature and location, they are of much greater significance than ice-scoured plains. In the United States, most of the broad outer margins of the glaciated regions are classed as till plains. This unsorted glacial debris, which has been deposited beneath the ice surface, is sometimes called a *ground moraine*. Hummocky deposits of material at the outer limit of the ice are called *terminal moraines*. *Recessional moraines* are similar in form to terminal moraines, but are formed along a line of temporary readvance after a major ice retreat. *Interlobate moraines* are formed between tongues or lobes of the ice. Mountain and valley glaciers also have terminal moraines, ground moraines, and recessional moraines, and in addition *lateral moraines*—glacial debris which marks the edges of the ice along the valley sides. When two glaciers unite the lateral moraines may converge and coalesce to form a *medial moraine*.

Small hillocks of debris, resembling an egg cut in two lengthwise are called *drumlins*. Drumlins have a long axis parallel to the direction of ice movement with the steeper end facing the direction from which the ice came. The formation of drumlins is not completely understood, but they usually occur in groups in areas between the terminal and recessional moraines.

Glacial meltwater is also responsible for the formation of a significant array of landform features. An important feature of these glacio-fluvial deposits is that they are composed of roughly stratified materials. A sloping plane formed at the ice margin by the deposits of glacial streams is called an *outwash plain*. An analogous feature in mountain and valley glaciers is called a *valley train*. A sinuous ridge of material formed by a stream flowing beneath the surface of the ice is called an *esker*. Small conical shaped hills of debris deposited by streams at, or near, the ice margin are called *kames*. Occasionally ice-blocks will be covered by glacial material and after melting, the depression which is left is known as a *kettle*. Glacial lakes, when drained, often show fine-grained banded deposits whose banded structures are referred to as *varves*.

Continental ice sheets frequently block pre-existent streams and force them to cut new channels. Such channels are called *glacial spillways or urströmtaler*.

Poorly drained depressions containing lakes and swamps are very abundant in many areas once covered by ice sheets. Sometimes they are caused by irregular deposition of till. Others commonly result from diversion of some previously existing stream and a complete rearrangement of the drainage pattern.

WIND DEPOSITS Wind deposits are characterized by sorted grains which are unstratified. Most dry areas are left with coarser materials over rocks as finer materials have been removed. Wind driven materials grind the surface until an exposed face is worn away. If the rock changes position another flat surface is developed in the same way. Thus, the number and shape of facets vary, but a common form of wind blasted pebble is elongate with three faces that taper toward sharp corners.

Landforms produced by wind erosion are of two types: (1) accumulation of sand called dunes; and (2) thick deposits of fine-grained materials called *loess*.

Particles rolled along the ground are commonly deposited in mounds and short ridges known as *sand dunes*. Dunes may begin to accumulate where any obstruction such as fence, bush, or boulder lessens wind velocities. Once started, the dune itself acts as an obstruction and grows larger as more sand is deposited. Dunes are usually less than 50 feet in height, but some attain heights of several hundred feet.

Sand dunes are most abundant along the shores of lakes and seas, on or near the flood plains of rivers, and in areas where ancient sandstones are disintegrating. Under various conditions, dunes display a variety of shapes. Where winds are variable rather than constant in direction, as is generally true in the United States, dune topography is characterized by irregularly shaped and variously distributed hills or mounds. Crescent-shaped dunes are called *barchans*. Wave-like dunes, which occur where sand is especially abundant are called *transverse dunes*. Extensive sandy deserts, which are the result of wind deposition (inflation), are called *ergs*. Where sand supplies are meager, long dune ridges parallel to the prevailing wind direction form. These are termed *longitudinal dunes*.

Very fine dust may be carried in suspension by wind for long distances. Sometimes fine dust forms a thin, indistinguishable veneer which levels landforms as it covers them. Accumulations of dust particles in great depths are known as *loess*. Loess is deposited mostly along river banks and around desert margins. Certain of the world's rich soils are formed from loess, but moisture retention is difficult because they are highly porous. Vast areas of loess are found in North China, central portions of the U.S., and in the Pampas of Argentina.

MARINE DEPOSITS Marine sediments are generally sorted so that the coarser materials are deposited near shore and grade into finer material seaward. They usually consist of rounded sediments which have been eroded from coast lines or river-born sediments which have been deposited in the form of onshore or offshore features.

Onshore features take several characteristic forms. Sometimes sediment is transported by waves and currents into bays forming beaches. Continuous erosion by undercurrents frequently redeposits them farther out as bars or terraces. Gradually sloping shorelines with shallow waters cause waves to drop sediments farther out from shore as *offshore bars*. But by wave erosion, these ridges also disappear or migrate. A variety of other bars may form along coastlines and are typically named in terms of their position with respect to the coast. For example, bars may be called *baymouth bars, bayhead bars,* or *midbay bars*. Occasionally sand bars may tie an island to the shore. Such a composite feature is called a *tombolo*. *Spits* and *hooks* are close relatives of bars.

STUDY QUESTIONS

1. Enumerate several ways in which man has aided the natural agents of disintegration.

2. Which agent of erosion is primarily responsible for the following features?

   (a) beach
   (b) sinks
   (c) sand dune
   (d) natural levee
   (e) loess

   (f) moraines
   (g) till
   (h) delta
   (i) outwash plain
   (j) alluvial fan

   (k) striated surfaces
   (l) kames
   (m) kettles
   (n) karst
   (o) flood plain

3. Which age cycle of erosion (youth, maturity, or old age) is most characteristic of the following features?

   (a) V-shaped stream valleys
   (b) Modified U-shaped stream valleys
   (c) Streams with abundant water-falls and rapids
   (d) Numerous stream meanders
   (e) Streams with limited development of flood plains
   (f) Ox-bow lakes
   (g) Many large streams and numerous tributaries

4. Account for the differences in the shape of a stream valley originally eroded by ice and one eroded by running water.

5. Describe the changes in the features of a well-developed stream from the mouth to its headwaters.

6. State the principal characteristics of deposits from running water, ice, wind, and the ocean. Give size and shape characteristics and whether or not they are sorted and stratified.

7. Draw a circle diagram of the zones which make up the earth's interior.

8. Give the main characteristics of sedimentary, metamorphic, and igneous rocks.

9. List and discuss some catastrophic volcanic eruptions.

10. Differentiate between a rock and a mineral.

SELECTED REFERENCES

Lake, P. *Physical Geography* (London: Cambridge University Press, 1949).

Lobeck, A. K. *Geomorphology: An Introduction to the Study of Landscapes* (New York: McGraw-Hill Book Co., Inc., 1939).

Seeman, A. L. *Physical Geography* (New York: Prentice-Hall, Inc., 1942), pp. 96-247.

Strahler, A. N. *Physical Geography* (New York: John Wiley and Sons, Inc., 2nd Edition, 1960).

Thornbury, W. D. *Principles of Geomorphology* (New York: John Wiley and Sons, Inc., 1954).

Chapter Eight

TYPES AND DISTRIBUTION OF LANDFORMS

Each of the seven continents has a definite arrangement of landforms which, along with size and shape, gives it distinguishing characteristics. These landforms may be grouped into four generally homogeneous types despite a wide variety of differences. The major landforms are designated as plains, plateaus, hills, and mountains.

PLAINS

Plains are areas of low relief and mostly low elevations of less than 2,000 feet. The local relief (difference in elevation between the highest and lowest points) is generally less than 500 feet. Within this limit, plains may be inclined or nearly flat, but they are generally relatively level. Plains may be classified on the basis of climatic characteristics. To illustrate, they may be termed: humid tropical plains, arid tropical plains, or subarctic plains. Another and normally more useful classification is based upon the roughness, or relief, of the plain. Plains thus classified by Finch and Trewartha are termed: (1) flat plains, which have a local relief of less than 50 feet; (2) undulating plains, which have a local relief of 50 to 150 feet; (3) rolling planes, which have a local relief of 150 to 300 feet; and (4) rough dissected plains, which have a local relief of 300 to 500 feet. Finally, plains may be categorized according to the dominant agents and processes which have shaped them. For example, there are stream-eroded plains, stream-deposited plains, wind-deposited plains, and structural plains. Regardless of these different systems of classification, however, most plains are lower than neighboring areas of plateaus, hills, and mountains. The surfaces of plateaus, however, in some instances can be termed plains and placed in a special category known as high plains.

Structural plains may be composed of a great variety of materials and may have been developed under different conditions, but such plains typically represent portions of continents which have emerged from the sea. If crustal disturbances have been minimal, flat-lying or gently dipping sediments become plains after emergence from the sea. Such plains may be quite close to the coast, as in the Atlantic and Gulf Coastal Plain of the United States, whereas others, such as the Great Plains and Interior Lowlands of North America are located at some distance in the interior. Agencies of erosion and deposition, previously cited, may produce significant plains regions. For example glaciation may modify pre-existent surfaces either by ice-scour, ice deposition, or both, converting irregular surfaces into plains. The erosive and depositional aspects of running water and wind may also yield plains surfaces. Deltas, alluvial fans, and flood plains are all examples of small plains formed by water deposition. Water erosion may reduce large areas to, or almost to, base level. Such a feature is called a *peneplain,* but it represents a stream-eroded plain.

Most of the world's people live on plains. These extensive lowlands are well adapted for human activities. Civilization evolved principally on plains, and still flourishes in plains regions, because of their many inherent advantages for agriculture, transportation, manufacturing, and trade. A study of the general distribution of the world's great plains shows that the majority of them are tributary to the Atlantic Ocean.

Some plains are adjacent to the Atlantic, as for example, the Argentine Pampa, the Atlantic Coastal Plain of the United States, and the plains of northwestern Europe. Others, such as the plains of northern Asia and northwestern Canada, are indirectly tributary to the Atlantic. To illustrate, the plains of Siberia although actually nearer to the Pacific Ocean, are separated from it by rugged mountains and plateaus. Their orientation is westward in the general direction of the Atlantic Ocean.

The general absence of substantial plains peripheral to the Pacific Ocean is due in large part to the fact that this is a zone of crustal weakness where mountain building and vulcanism have been and are important. In contrast, the earth's structure at the margins of the Atlantic are relatively more stable; hence plains regions are subject to less deformation.

Several newly emerged plains in the United States, geologically speaking, are the coastal regions of Virginia, the Carolinas, Georgia, and parts of the coast extending from Florida to Texas. Most of these are flat plains with a relief of less than 50 feet. Other newly emerged plains are located along the Arctic fringes of Alaska and in the Soviet Union, east and west of the Ural Mountains.

Large glaciated plains are found in north-central North America and northwestern Europe, while flood plains flank large rivers, such as the Mississippi and the Amazon.

Oscillating sea levels cause considerable areal change in plains fringing the sea. For example, a fall in sea level of a few feet would add thousands of square miles of territory to the United States as portions of the continental shelf would be exposed. Conversely, a rise in sea level of a few feet would submerge lands of the Atlantic and Gulf Coastal Plains of the United States.

Although the foregoing treatment of the distribution of plains is sketchy in the extreme, examination of maps of population, agriculture, manufacturing, and transportation facilities reveals an almost direct correlation between plains regions and intensity of human use of the land. High productivity and plains regions are usually directly related.

PLATEAUS

Plateaus are broad uplands of considerable elevation usually more than 2,000 feet above sea level which rise abruptly on at least one side above the adjacent area. The relief generally exceeds that of plains, and often plateau surfaces are trenched with deep valleys or canyons. Nevertheless, a considerable part of plateau surfaces are at or near the highest level of elevation, and maintain the appearances of tabular uplands. Plateaus normally stand above neighboring plains and are separated from them at some points by abrupt slopes. A few plateaus (such as the Patagonian Plateau in Argentina) reach almost to the seacoast and are terminated by a sudden drop to the water level. In most cases, however, plateaus have interior locations and are bordered by mountains, hills, or plains rather than seas.

The plateaus of the earth are basically of three major types according to their position. They are termed: (1) *intermontane plateaus,* which are uplifted segments of the earth's crust surrounded by mountains; (2) *piedmont plateaus,* which are situated between mountains and bordering plains or seas; (3) *continental plateaus* (tablelands) which rise abruptly from bordering lowlands or from seas and generally have no contiguous mountain rims.

In tropical climates, certain plateaus of South America and Africa are densely populated, because increased elevation results in lower temperatures which are suitable to human activities. By contrast, in temperate and polar climates, practically all plateaus are sparsely populated, because they are frequently too cold or too dry. Generally, plateaus are transportation barriers because deeply-cut stream valleys are apt to present difficult road or rail building problems. Normally an abrupt change in slope to lower plains or higher mountains also produces a transportation hindrance. In general, plateaus are considered unfavorable for human habitation, except where minerals are abundant or hot climates are tempered.

Many intermontane plateaus are located between ranges of the Andes Mountains, in the western part of Mongolia, and in the Tarim Basin of Asia. Other intermontane plateaus are found in central Mexico and between the Rocky Mountains and the Sierra Nevada and Cascade Mountains of the United States.

The Colorado Plateau of the United States is basically an example of the piedmont type. Numerous examples of piedmont plateaus can be found in Utah, along the Great Salt Lake, in California near Mono Lake, in the eastern part of the United States at the base of the Blue Ridge, and in northern Italy at the foot of the Alps.

Continental plateaus or tablelands can be found in portions of Africa, Arabia, Spain, parts of Australia, peninsular India, and ice-covered Greenland and Antarctica. Often Africa is called a continental plateau because most of its territory is made up of a series of tablelands.

Plateaus may also be classified in terms of their structural characteristics. For example most of the plateaus in the world can logically be classified as: (1) *lava,* (2) *horizontal sedimentary,* or (3) *disordered crystalline.* Some of the best examples of plateaus built up by great outpourings of lava are the Columbia Plateau of northwestern United States, the Deccan Plateau of western peninsular India, and the Paraná Plateau of southern Brazil. The Colorado Plateau of southwestern United States is an excellent example of a plateau made up principally of flat-lying sedimentary rocks. The Plateau of western Australia, the American Piedmont Plateau, and the Laurentian Shield are composed of disordered crystalline rock.

HILLS

Those regions which are at an elevation greater than 500 feet and are generally too rough and have too much relief to be called plains, but at the same time have too little relief to be called mountains, are classified as hills. For this reason, hills are sometimes difficult to distinguish from rough plains or low mountain regions. Actually they are transition zones between rough plains and low mountains. Arbitrarily, hills can be considered to embrace those areas where more than one-half the area is in slopes rather than in upland or lowland flats and whose local relief is more than 500 feet but less than 2,000 feet. The habitability of hills is less than that of plains regions but usually greater than that of mountainous areas. People are apt to be confined to the upland or lowland flats, because these offer good possibilities for agriculture and construction of transportation routes.

Hills are definitely different from both rolling and rough plains in that they have considerably greater relief. They are markedly different from plateaus because they are more dissected and they have smaller upland surfaces and a greater percentage of their area in slopes. In some cases, they resemble mountain regions because relief may be great, and much of the land may be in steep slopes. Often rough hills are mountain-like in comparison with adjoining plains and are mistakenly called mountains. However, in most hill regions the terrain is less complicated, and their detailed features are of a smaller order of size than those of mountains. Hills may be produced through structural movements, such as folding and faulting, or they may evolve through dissection of upland surfaces by stream erosion.

In humid climatic regions, progress of the stream erosion cycle is rapid; and mature dissection by streams and their tributaries carves the original upland surface into a mass of hills and valleys. Hills resulting from rapid erosion are found in that part of the western Appalachian Mountains called the Allegheny-Cumberland region, extending from northern Pennsylvania to northeastern Alabama. The well-known Badlands of South Dakota are hills which have resulted from erosion over a long period of time. The Ozarks of southern Missouri and northern Arkansas are hill remnants of a dissected upland plateau surface.

Many hills consist of intermingled rock of different origins and highly complicated structure. Examples of this type of hill region are found in the Palisades area of the Hudson River. The Central Highlands of Germany are hill and plateau regions resulting from stream dissection of uplands which are underlain by a variety of rock types. Hills characterized by ridges and valleys of linear and roughly parallel patterns are represented by the folded Appalachians of eastern United States and the Ouachitas of Oklahoma and Arkansas.

Eastern Asia has the greatest expanse of hill land. This area includes portions of Siberia, Manchuria, Central and South China, Central India, and most of Korea and Japan. Other hilly areas of considerable extent include the ice-scoured or glaciated hills in eastern Canada, the highlands of Scotland, Scandinavia, and the Adirondacks of New York.

MOUNTAINS

Mountains are areas of high elevation (above 3,000 feet), with small summit area and with most of their surface in slopes having a relief greater than 2,000 feet. Mountains have nothing in common with plains and very little in common with plateaus unless the plateaus are extremely and deeply dissected.

A combination of both diastrophic and volcanic forces, along the extensive and somewhat indefinite margins of the outer crust of the earth, has produced mountain uplifts of great variety in shape, size, and arrangement. These mountains are attacked by the agents of weathering and erosion and are carved into a great variety of features. Mountains also result from erosion of domed structures, which are caused by giant intrusions of igneous rock that have arched the earth's surface upward. The overlying sedimentary rocks upon such an intrusion may be removed almost entirely by erosion, and ranges and valleys of radial pattern may be eroded in the massive rocks beneath. Mountains may be formed when wrinkles in the earth's crust in the shape of folds develop because of lateral tension or compression. Local deformations are caused by a combination of shrinkages of the crust of the earth. Cooling, compaction, and varying densities of crust and mantle are primarily responsible for the shrinkages.

Mountain construction through extrusive flows of lava or ashfalls derived from volcanoes are well known, but the effects of intrusive vulcanism in mountain building are more subtle. Giant ig-

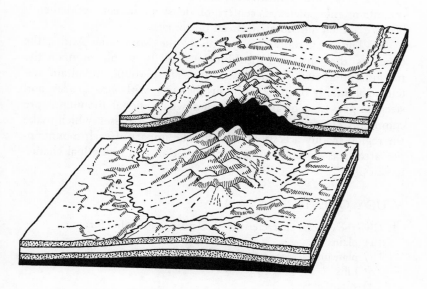

*Fig. 14   A domed structure which has been eroded
into mountainous terrain*

neous intrusions, called *batholiths,* may cause the earth's crust above to be warped up to form mountains. Smaller, toadstool-shaped igneous intrusions called *laccoliths* may produce small, less prepossessing mountains. Variety in different types of terrain may be caused by smaller igneous intrusions. *Dikes* are intruded into cracks in rock, whereas *sills* are intruded between layers of sedimentary rocks or sequential lava flows. *Stocks* or *bosses* are irregular intrusions of intermediate size which may cause the development of small hills. *Plugs* or *necks* of solidified lava may fill the vent of a dormant volcano. Intrusive volcanic features are of significance to the geographer when they cause a bulge or wrinkle observable at the surface or when they are exposed due to erosion.

When mountains in mid-latitudes are densely populated they are usually recreational, lumbering, or mining areas. These settlements are often abandoned when forest or mineral resources are exhausted. Man usually avoids mountains, because they are barriers to easy human movement. Only in equatorial highlands are mountains, like plateaus, centers of dense permanent settlements, because of their ameliorative effects on climate.

The great mountain systems of the world; the Andes, the Cascades, the Alps, and the Himalayas all lie within or upon the margins of known crustal instability. These young mountain systems commonly form continuous barriers with few passes and steep slopes. In contrast, old worn-down erosional mountains are commonly characterized by water gaps or other passes, which make the region readily accessible. The specific impact of each mountainous area is as variable as its precise location and individual characteristics.

STUDY QUESTIONS

1. Give the general characteristics of elevation and relief for:
   (a) plains
   (b) plateaus
   (c) hills
   (d) mountains
2. On which type of major landform do you live? Describe the relief and elevation of your locality.

3. Explain why there is a high degree of direct correlation between intensive human use and plains.
4. Differentiate between a continental plateau and an intermontane plateau. Give an example of each.
5. What is the predominant type of landform in the following areas?
   (a) East Coast of the United States
   (b) Florida
   (c) Badlands of South Dakota
   (d) Western South America
   (e) Western Kentucky
6. What economic activities are most commonly followed in mid-latitude mountains?
7. Why are tropical plateaus often more densely populated than tropical plains?
8. List several causes of mountain building.
9. Name the great mountain systems of the world.
10. Contrast the characteristics of the Appalachian Mountains with those of the Rocky Mountains.

SELECTED REFERENCES

Atwood, W. W. *The Physiographic Provinces of North America* (New York: Ginn and Co., 1940).

Durand, L., Jr. *World Geography* (New York: Henry Holt and Co., 1954), pp. 1-77.

Fenneman, N. M. *Physiography of Eastern United States* (New York: McGraw-Hill Book Co., Inc., 1938).

Fenneman, N. M. *Physiography of Western United States* (New York: McGraw-Hill Book Co., Inc., 1931).

Peattie, Roderick. *Mountain Geography* (Cambridge: Harvard University Press, 1936).

von Engeln, O. D. *Geomorphology, Systematic and Regional* (New York: The Macmillan Co., 1942).

Wooldridge, S. W. and Morgan, R. S. *Outlines of Geomorphology* (New York: Longmans, Green and Co., Inc., 1937).

Chapter Nine

SOILS

Top soil which blankets the terrestrial globe is perhaps man's most precious resource. Eons of time are required to form soil which may be lost quickly. To replace it will require scores or even hundreds of years. Soil science (*pedology*) is fundamental to an understanding of geography, since soils are an integral part of the physical and cultural landscape.

NATURE OF SOIL

It is no simple matter to define soil, a highly complex organic material. Soil is normally considered to be composed of minerals, organic compounds, living organisms, air, and water. The soil zone is that portion of the terrestrial globe which supports plant growth. Each of the constituent elements plays an integral part in determining soil characteristics, utility, and productivity. Dynamic chemical and biologic changes, constantly operative, make soil a developing and changing substance.

MINERALS The amount and type of mineral matter in soil varies greatly from place to place. Many factors control the nature of the content. One of the most significant of these is parent material. For example, a soil developing from a limestone ($CaCO_3$) bedrock will contain minerals different from those in a soil which develops from sandstone (SiO_2).

A knowledge of mineral content is important in ascertaining the inherent productivity of a soil. Plants require a great number of minerals for growth, but only a few are used in large amounts. Those most commonly depleted from soil are *nitrogen, phosphorous,* and *potassium.* These minerals are frequently replaced by the use of commercial and/or organic fertilizer. Certain other minerals, known as *trace elements* are necessary for plant growth, but their function in plant nutrition is, as yet debatable. Some of the most significant trace elements are *boron, copper,* and *antimony.*

ORGANIC COMPOUNDS *Humus,* which breaks down into organic compounds, is composed of semidecayed remains of plant and animal life. These organic substances are extremely useful in soils since they improve *tilth* (workability), aid in water retention, provide a home for living organisms, and replenish minerals.

LIVING ORGANISMS When soil is examined closely it is found to be the habitat of millions of animals. The larger animals, *macroorganisms,* such as earthworms, ants, and beetles are useful in soil, since their tunnels afford avenues for aeration and water movement. In addition, certain animals such as the earthworm take particles of soil through their digestive tract. Some authorities contend, however, that earthworms and similar animals are present in fertile soil but contribute little to it. Organic acids cause particles to be broken down, and as a result minerals in the soil are made more readily usable for plants. *Micro-organisms* (animals invisible to the naked eye) cause the decay of organic material and speed the disintegration and decomposition of minerals, thus making nutrients available for plants.

AIR AND WATER Air and water are as essential to plants as to animals. Since plants are rooted in the soil they are dependent upon it for most of their water requirements. A soil's capacity for holding water depends mainly upon its porosity (amount of porous space in the soil). If the soil is excessively porous it will not retain water, whereas if it is impervious (compact), water cannot be absorbed.

Water is present in soil as gravitational water, capillary water, and hygroscopic water. *Gravitational water* percolates downward, due to the pull of gravity, between the individual soil particles or aggregates of soil particles completely filling the pore spaces. Gravitational water is present in largest amounts immediately after rains.

Capillary water is the water which is held by surface tension upon soil particles and occupies portions of the pore spaces. Under varying climatic conditions capillary water may move downward, laterally, or even upward in much the same way as oil in a kerosene lamp moves in the direction of greatest capillary tension. Since such water is useful to plants its upward movement through fine-textured soils in periods of drought is of considerable significance.

Hygroscopic water is held as a microscopically thin film around each individual soil particle. This water is the last to be desiccated from soil. Actually, hygroscopic water frequently is removed from soil only after prolonged baking in a high temperature oven. Hygroscopic water is of no value to plants, since they cannot absorb it.

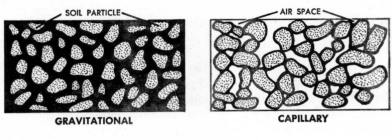

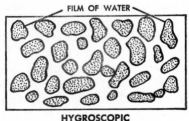

Fig. 15   How water is held in the soil

PHYSICAL AND CHEMICAL CHARACTERISTICS

Soil possesses certain readily observable physical character-istics. Among the most significant of these are *texture, structure, color,* and *depth.*

Soil texture (size of soil particles) may vary from very fine clays and silts to coarse sands and gravels. Soil texture is of geo-graphic significance, since it influences the tilth of the soil, the supply of plant nutrients, and the absorption and retention of air and water. For most types of plants a loamy texture (20 per cent or less of clay, 30-50 per cent of silt, and 30-50 per cent of sand) is the most satisfactory textural medium.

Soil structure refers to the manner in which individual soil particles tend to aggregate into larger clumps. For example, certain soils have a granular structure, a platy structure, or a lens-like structure. Soil structure largely determines root penetration, water absorption rates, erosion susceptibility, and tilth.

Deep soils are obviously better from an agricultural standpoint than thin soils, which may be buried by the subsoil when plowed. Deep soils similarly afford an opportunity for plant roots to make use of the mineral nutrients which are present.

Color of soils varies greatly from place to place. Parent material, minerals, and natural vegetation are the principal factors influencing soil color. Soil color may have subtle influences upon soil temperatures and hence upon plant growth. As a broad generalization, however, soil color is an index of the amount of organic matter present. The darker soils usually have the greatest quantity of organic matter. In mid-latitudes soils typically range from dark brown or black in humid regions to light brown or gray on steppe or desert areas. Red or yellow colors usually result from iron oxide or hydroxide stains. Grayish or bluish colors in mid-latitude soils means the presence of reduced iron in the soil and typically occur in areas of poor drainage.

A very significant characteristic of soil relates to its chemical reaction. *Colloids,* very small particles of minerals or organic matter, can attract and hold ions. Certain basic ions are used by plants in their growth processes by a method known as *base exchange.* Hydrogen ions in the soil create conditions of acidity. The accumulation of hydrogen ions in the soil is known as the pH of the soil. A pH of 7.0 is considered neutral and low pH readings indicate soil acidity, whereas high pH readings are indications of soil alkalinity. Most useful agricultural plants do best in a neutral or slightly alkaline soil. Certain acid fruits, such as cranberries and gooseberries thrive in acid soils. The absolute range of high order plant growth occurs in the band from pH 4.0 to pH 10.0.

SOIL PROFILES

Most of the earth's soils are developed from weathered rock. As weathering results in rock disintegration and decomposition, plants and animals are able to establish a foothold. The evolution of soil begins when life forms establish a foothold on weathered rock materials.

The principal result of soil forming processes is the development of layers in the *regolith* (weathered bedrock). These layers (*horizons*) are different physically and chemically, but they all evolve from the same rock materials (parent materials). A cross section through these layers is known as a *soil profile*. Only mature soils exhibit a complete soil profile.

The top layer is known as the *A-horizon* (topsoil). The A-horizon is a zone which is subject to loss through removal of materials in suspension (*eluviation*) or by solution (*leaching*). Similarly the A-horizon is the zone of heaviest humus accumulation and normally the most fertile portion.

Immediately below the A-horizon is a zone of accumulation of materials, which were removed from the A-horizon. This zone, the *B-horizon,* is more compact than the A-horizon, and contains little or no humus. The A-horizon and B-horizon together form the soil proper.

Fragmented particles of weathered bedrock immediately below the B-horizon constitute the *C-horizon*. The *D-horizon* is composed of unweathered rock material below the C-horizon. Bedrock underlies the D-horizon.

Boundaries between soil horizons may be sharp or indistinct, regular or irregular. It should be noted, too, that one or more horizons may be missing from a given profile. Erosion may remove the topsoil and subsoil horizons or the C-horizon may be non-existent as the D-horizon weathers directly into the B-horizon. In addition, individual horizons are often subdivided on the basis of slight differences. For example, the A-horizon may be subdivided into A^1, A^2, and A^3.

SOIL FORMING PROCESSES

Soil is formed from the regolith, and a great variety and

combination of factors unite to produce a particular soil type. The most important of these factors are *parent material, climate, natural vegetation, living organisms, slope,* and *time.* Obviously, the significance of each factor varies tremendously from place to place.

To illustrate, it should be self-evident that a soil formed on sandstone, under tropical rainforest climate and vegetation conditions, with many living organisms actively working on a flat surface for a long period of time will vary tremendously from one which has developed on limestone under desert climate, sparse vegetation, a paucity of living organisms, a steep slope, and a minimum of time. In spite of the myriad combination of factors influencing soil development three processes, *latozation, podsolization,* and *calcification,* serve to explain the existence of mature soil varieties from place to place.

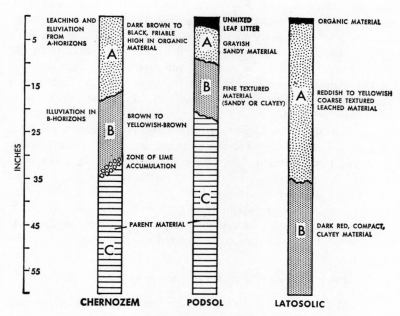

Fig. 16 Soil profiles representative of the principal soil forming processes

LATOZATION Latozation occurs most commonly in humid tropical and humid subtropical regions. Leaching and eluviation are developed to a high degree, i.e. materials are removed in solution and suspension from the topsoil resulting in a coarse granular topsoil and a compact subsoil. Leaching is normally intense. This results in the removal of most mineral materials from the topsoil except aluminum and iron compounds. Organic material is generally limited or lacking in amount because high temperatures and high moisture content together with an abundance of living organisms cause rapid decay of humus. One outstanding feature of latozation is the development of reddish or yellowish colors in soil. Since rock deterioration is rapid, latozation results in the development of deep soils.

PODSOLIZATION Podsolization occurs in cool, moist severe, or moist temperate environments which are forested. Animal life in the soil is meager, and, as a result, there is little mixing of organic material with the mineral matter in soil. Slow decay results in an accumulation of a peaty mat of acid organic material on the soil's surface. Leaching of the topsoil results in a sandy mixture in the A-horizon. The subsoil is compact and frequently clayey, because of the deposit of small particles of material which were removed from the topsoil. Podsolization usually results in the development of shallow, acid soils.

CALCIFICATION Unlike latozation and podsolization, calcification occurs in subhumid to semiarid climatic environments under grass vegetation. Because precipitation is light, leaching and eluviation are at a minimum. Calcium accumulates in the upper horizons of the soil, since grasses, when dead, yield the calcium which they have accumulated. Animal life and organic material are present in abundance. Calcified soils test neutral or basic (sweet in chemical reaction), while latozized and podsolized soils are chemically acidic (sour).

SOIL CLASSIFICATION

Mature soils exhibit certain characteristics when developed under a specific combination of the various soil-forming factors. Major categories of soils are the end products of soil-forming processes over a long period of time in a given area.

Zonal soils are those which have well-developed character-istics in particular response to climate and natural vegetation, and, as such, are found widely distributed in areas of similar climate and vegetation. *Intrazonal* soils have developed primarily because of parent material or age control, and, therefore, may be present in widely different climatic and vegetation areas. *Azonal* soils are immature soils which have no well-developed soil profile, as for example, loess and alluvium.

Since zonal soils exhibit a rational worldwide pattern, at-tention will be directed in the next chapter to the great soil groups in the zonal category. Obvious relationships between soil, climate, and vegetation will be made apparent.

CLIMAX SOILS Some soils experts hold the theory that under identical climatic and other physical circumstances, given time enough, no matter what the nature of the parent material, there will be no difference in the kind of soil formed.

STUDY QUESTIONS

1. Differentiate the general characteristics of topsoil and subsoil.
2. List the major materials which make up soil.
3. Explain the difference between soil texture and soil structure.
4. What are the main factors in the formation of a particular soil type?
5. Explain or define the following:

   Latozation   Podsolization   Intrazonal soils
   Calcification   Zonal soils   Azonal soils

6. Classify the soils in your locality as to:

   (a) texture   (b) color   (c) origin   (d) structure

7. What methods are used in your locality for improving soil fertility?
8. How does crop rotation help to maintain soil fertility?
9. What is meant by the soil profile?
10. Using a soil augur or spade dig to a depth which delineates the A and B horizon. How can you distinguish the boundary? Which horizon is more compact? Which is darker in color?

Chapter Ten

MAJOR SOIL REGIONS OF THE WORLD

The great soil groups are divided into two classes, the *pedocals* and *pedalfers*. Pedocals are calcium accumulating soils which develop in semiarid or arid climatic regions. Pedalfers are aluminum and iron accumulating soils which develop in humid environments. The most significant of the pedalfers are: latosolic, tropical red, red earth, gray-brown podsol, podsol, prairie, and tundra soils. The most important of the pedocals are: chernozems, chestnut earths, brown earths, and desert soils.

PEDALFERS

LATOSOLIC SOILS The soils which are the most weathered and most leached are called latosolic soils. These soils are found typically in tropical rainforest climates, where the rainfall exceeds 75-80 inches annually and where there is no definite dry season. Many authorities also report the presence of such soils in tropical savanna regions. Latosolic soils are made up of end products of weathering such as silicates, hydrous oxides of aluminum, and iron oxides from which most of the water soluble materials have been removed. Latosolic soils are very low in humus and this lack of humus along with the prevalence of aluminum and iron compounds accounts for the yellowish to reddish color. After two or three years of use, the small amount of humus present is consumed by various plants, broken down by certain chemical reactions, and carried away by the ground water. Organic material is limited or almost completely lacking. The topsoil is usually coarse textured, porous, and subject to rapid oxidation. Subsoils are normally compact, frequently clayey, and reddish or yellowish in color. Latosolic soils are poor agricultural soils.

Under certain conditions extreme leaching and eluviation in tropical regions produces a soil which is brick-like in character and practically sterile. Such materials, not soil in the strictest sense, are very restricted in area and are called *laterites*. If it were possible to remove the poor topsoil material by erosion or other means, the subsoil in latosolic soil zones would be more productive than the original topsoil.

TROPICAL RED SOILS Another pedalfer, the tropical red soil, is a variety of latosolic soil. These soils are located in certain areas of tropical rainforests, in tropical savannas, and tropical monsoon environments. The tropical red soils are not so thoroughly leached as true latosols. Since they have developed under a grass or mixed grass and tree cover, they have a higher humus content. The higher humus and mineral content make the tropical red soils somewhat more fertile than the heavily leached laterites or latosolic soils. Important grazing regions have developed in areas of tropical red soils. They will continue to increase in importance when better transportation methods are developed, improved breeds of animals are utilized, and tropical diseases are eliminated. Judicious additions of minerals and organic fertilizers may make them reasonably productive as agricultural soils.

RED EARTH SOILS The red earth soils, which are associated with humid subtropical climates, are distinguishable from other soil groups by their color and other physical characteristics. They possess only limited amounts of humus, since they have evolved under forest cover where rapid decay quickly consumes leaf litter. Heavy rainfall facilitates rapid leaching, leaving the red earths low in lime and other readily soluble minerals. Because of alternate freezing and thawing in humid subtropical winters, these soils are subjected to constant seepage and erosion. Soil erosion has had disastrous consequences in many such regions, which have been unwisely cultivated. Indeed some areas, like Stewart County, Georgia, have become man-made badlands. With proper care, however, red earth soils can be used effectively for certain diversified agricultural purposes if an adequate ground cover is maintained and mineral and organic fertilizers are added periodically.

GRAY-BROWN PODSOLS Gray-brown podsols are shallower, have

more organic matter, are less leached, and are inherently more fertile than latosolic, tropical red, or red earth soils. The A-horizon is grayish-brown in color, leached, and moderately coarse textured. The B-horizon is darker brown and finer textured. Gray-brown earths are associated with humid continental climates, and because they are located further poleward they are not subject to as much constant leaching and weathering as the latosolic, tropical reds, and red earths. Since the falling leaves do not oxidize as readily as those in the tropical or subtropical climates, more humus is added to the upper horizons of these soils. The gray-brown earths also contain more lime, potash, and a variety of other minerals. Because of the higher humus content and the brown stain from iron hydroxide, these soils have a darker color. The soils are also more fertile and contain less acid than soils which are laterized. Due to their favorable structure and generally excellent composition their productivity can be increased more easily by proper cultivation, rotation, fertilization, deeper plowing, subsoiling, liming, and other improvements. Much of the productive area of the Middle Atlantic and Great Lakes States is composed of this kind of soil.

PODSOL SOILS Podsol soils are found on the poleward margins of humid continental climates and in subarctic climates. They occupy chiefly the northern borders of the United States extending from the Upper Great Lakes to New England, Northern Eurasia, parts of southern Chile, and the coast of New Zealand. Podosols form in a humid climate with low temperatures and under coniferous or mixed forest conditions. Because they have no well-defined structure and lack an abundant supply of essential minerals, their fertility cannot be easily improved. Their contribution, however, to grazing regions and recreational areas cannot be overlooked. Podsols are characterized by a thin surface layer of raw humus, an ash gray coarse textured A-horizon, and a compact yellowish-brown B-horizon. Living organisms are few in numbers in this type soil primarily because of its strong acid reaction.

PRAIRIE SOILS Prairie soils are typically dark brown in color. Leaching is slight, organic matter is present in large amounts, and inherent fertility is high. Soil depth varies from three to five feet, and color becomes lighter at increasing depths. Prairie soils are located in the more humid areas adjacent to the chernozem, or black earth soil regions, in the central part of the United States, Argentina, Manchuria, and sections of Africa. Even though their color is dark, they contain very little lime and other alkaline substances. While prairie soil color is typically dark brown, in certain regions the underlying bedrock may stain it another shade. For example, the redbeds of Oklahoma have influenced the development of reddish prairie soils in central Oklahoma. Their favorable structures and relatively high humus content make them excellent agricultural soils which can easily be maintained. Prairie earths normally develop in areas which receive 25 to 35 inches of precipitation and where the rate of evaporation is not excessive. Original natural vegetation of these soil zones is tall prairie grass. The relative abundance of moisture in these areas greatly enhances the agricultural productivity of prairie soils. Recently, conservation practices (terracing and contour stripcropping) have materially increased productivity of prairie soils.

TUNDRA SOILS Tundra soils are of little agricultural value. For eight to ten months each year they remain frozen, and during the brief period of summer, they thaw out only on the surface. Often these soils are water-logged, primarily because underneath them is *permafrost* (permanently frozen subsoil), which eliminates percolation of moisture from the surface to lower levels. Agricultural utilization of these soils is negligible because of their sterility and the restrictions to plant growth imposed by a severe climatic environment. Inhabitants of tundra soil areas depend mainly upon animal life (instead of vegetables and grain cereals) for their food. Tundra soils are exceptionally thin and strongly acid in reaction. The surface color is usually grayish with a considerable quantity of organic matter mixed within the A-horizon. Tundra soils are distributed throughout the tundra climatic regions of the world.

PEDOCALS

CHERNOZEM SOILS OR BLACK EARTHS The chernozem or black earth soils are located in subhumid grasslands of the middle latitudes. Some evidence suggests that chernozems, or chernozem-like, soils may be present in some abundance in tropical grasslands as well. Because of the small amount of leaching and the high humus content these soils are among the most fertile in the world. Due to their extremely high water holding capacity chernozems support an abundant growth of natural grasses as well as crops such as wheat, barley, and rye. Complete utilization is impossible because of infrequent, unreliable, and spotty precipitation. Chernozem soils are very slightly leached, high in available minerals, rich in humus, and very fertile. Their color grades from black at the surface to light brown or gray in the subsoil. A zone of lime accumulation is found typically two to three feet beneath the surface.

CHESTNUT EARTHS The chestnut earths, like the chernozem soils, have developed under a grass cover, but their color is not as dark. The humus content is small because there is an incomplete cover of natural grass. These soils are very fertile, in part because they are only slightly leached. The zone of lime accumulation is found somewhat closer to the surface than in the chernozem soils. The rainfall is light and erratic, and as a result, alkaline substances are present in abundance. Most chestnut earth soil areas are used for grazing and dry farming. Dry farming techniques are designed to make full use of soil moisture through mulching, deep plowing, raising crops in alternate years, and other techniques. The spring wheat region of the Prairie Provinces of Canada and the northern Great Plains of the United States lies in part in the chestnut earth areas and in part in the chernozem regions.

BROWN EARTHS The topsoil of the brown earths is brown in color, slightly leached, moderately well endowed with humus, and quite fertile. Colors lighten at increasing depths, and the zone of calcium accumulation is nearer the surface than in either chernozems or chestnut earths. Brown earths are normally found at the inner margins of steppe climates. Agricultural productivity is restricted by paucity of available moisture. They do not form a continuous zone. The mineral content of the brown earths is high, except for nitrogen, and their agricultural potential is excellent. The vegetation is composed of small clumps of grass and desert shrub. Grazing is the chief land use, except where irrigation is developed.

DESERT SOIL Desert soils are widely distributed throughout all the arid lands of the world. Desert soils have been subjected to little leaching and contain an abundance of soluble minerals. Although desert soils vary greatly from place to place, they are all characterized by a thin A-horizon, and a zone of calcium accumulation very close to the surface. Leaching is at a minimum because of a lack of moisture. The gray desert soil (*sierozem*) is one of the common soils encountered in desert regions. The chief forms of native plant life are desert shrubs with scattered clumps of grasses and herbs. The chief occupation in regions of desert soils is herding of sheep and goats, while cattle ranches are encountered at infrequent intervals. Desert soils may be highly productive, when water is made available, because of the abundance of essential plant nutrients. Agricultural possibilities are limited, but alfalfa and other feed crops can be grown under irrigation.

Soil Classification Soil classification involves generalization to a greater or lesser degree, since soils may vary considerably in very short distances. *Soil orders,* i.e., zonal soils, intrazonal soils, and azonal soils represent the greatest generalization recognized by pedologists. As the classification is made more specific, the orders are further divided into 10-12 *suborders.* Further division of the suborders is made into the *great soil groups.* Several of the most significant of these great soil groups have been described in the foregoing discussion. Division to this degree is sufficient for the purposes of this introductory study, but soil scientists would make a much more detailed breakdown. Great soil groups are divided into soil *families,* the families into *series,* and the series into *types.* The thousands of soil types may be further subdivided into *phases* on the basis of slope, stoniness, or some similar physical feature which might have a significant bearing upon their utilization for agricultural purposes.

Soils and Man Man depends for his food supply upon a topsoil which averages only six to eight inches in thickness. His past history of prodigality in dealing with his soil heritage is a shameful record. Soil erosion and leaching have become so significant that food supplies in many parts of the world are precariously short or inadequate. In addition, soil erosion creates problems of flooding; siltation of reservoirs, waterways, and harbors; damages to highways, and railroads; and sealing over and clogging of pores which

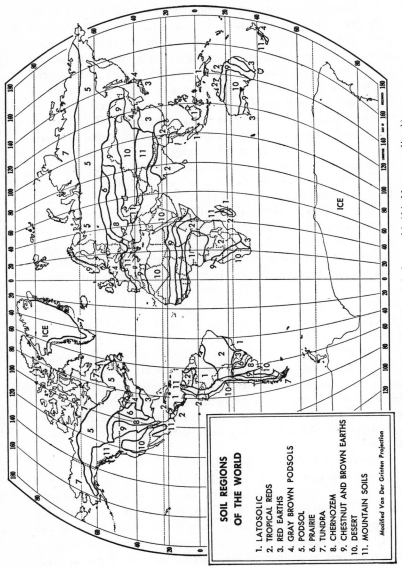

SOIL REGIONS
OF THE WORLD

1. LATOSOLIC
2. TROPICAL REDS
3. RED EARTHS
4. GRAY BROWN PODSOLS
5. PODSOL
6. PRAIRIE
7. TUNDRA
8. CHERNOZEM
9. CHESTNUT AND BROWN EARTHS
10. DESERT
11. MOUNTAIN SOILS

Modified Van Der Grinten Projection

Fig. 17 Principal soil regions of the world (highly generalized)

normally permit water to soak into the ground where it is badly needed.

Unwise soil practices result in the loss of more soil than nature can replace in thousands of years. The devastating effects of soil erosion have caused farm abandonment, rural migration, debts, poverty, and bankruptcy for many farmers. Its widespread adverse impact upon taxes, purchasing power, community life, and health are appalling. Soil conservation techniques now being implemented must be expanded in scope if the people of the world are to feed themselves in the face of a population growth which is increasing at an alarming rate.

STUDY QUESTIONS

1. What are the two great soil classes?
2. What are the great soil groups within each class?
3. Name the type of soil which predominates within the following climatic environments:

   (a) Subarctic   (e) Humid Continental
   (b) Humid Subtropical   (f) Inner margins of mid-latitude Steppe
   (c) Tundra   (g) Deserts
   (d) Tropical Rainforest   (h) Tropical Savanna

4. State the most common color of each of the following soil types:

   (a) Chernozems   (c) Desert Soils   (e) Podsols
   (b) Tundra Soils   (d) Latosols   (f) Prairie Soils

5. Name the type of soil most commonly found in these states:

   (a) Iowa   (c) Maine   (e) Arizona
   (b) Georgia   (d) Utah   (f) Ohio

SELECTED REFERENCES: CHAPTERS 9 AND 10

Ayres, Q. C. *Soil Erosion and Its Control* (New York: McGraw-Hill Book Co., Inc., 1936).

Bear, F. E. *Soils and Fertilizers* (New York: John Wiley and Sons, Inc., 1942).

Bennett, H. H. *Elements of Soil Conservation* (New York: McGraw-Hill Book Co., Inc., 1955).

Glinka, K. D. (translated by C. F. Marbut). *The Great Soil Groups of the World and Their Development* (Ann Arbor: Edwards Bros., Inc., 1927).

Gustafson, A. F., Guise, C. H., Hamilton, W. J., Jr. and Ries, H. *Conservation in the United States* (Ithaca: Comstock Publishing Co., 1949).

Jenny, H. *Factors of Soil Formation: A System of Quantitative Pedology* (New York: McGraw-Hill Book Co., Inc., 1941).

Kellog, C. E. *The Soils That Support Us* (New York: The Macmillan Co., 1941).

Peterson, E. T. *Forward to the Land* (Norman: University of Oklahoma Press, 1942).

Soil. Yearbook of Agriculture, 1957, United States Department of Agriculture, Washington, D.C.

Soils and Men. Yearbook of Agriculture, 1938, United States Department of Agriculture, Washington, D.C.

White, C. L. and Foscue, E. J. *Regional Geography of Anglo-America* (New York: Prentice-Hall, Inc., 2nd Edition, 1954), pp. 488-490.

Worthan, E. L. *Farm Soils* (New York: John Wiley and Sons, Inc., 1948).

Chapter Eleven ·

BIOTIC RESOURCES

Plants and animals reflect environmental relationships and thus are appropriate subjects for geographic investigation. Biotic phenomena are closely related to soil, slope, altitude, and climate. Climates are frequently named on the basis of associated natural vegetation. For example, the Af climate is termed tropical rainforest because rainforests are dominant types of vegetation in those climatic areas. All stands of natural vegetation are a consequence of evolutionary processes involving plant differentiation and adaptation during long periods of time.

The map of "Natural Vegetation Regions of the World" shows the distribution pattern of the major types of plant associations. Local variations may occur within these major types because of local differences in soil, surface configuration and drainage; but any significant change in the major plant associations reflects chiefly a difference in the principal climatic elements between the two areas. Low orders of vegetation are succeeded by higher types through a process known as *ecological succession.* Ultimately through natural selection and adaptation certain species of vegetation become dominant within a specific climatic region. Such vegetation is known as *climax vegetation.*

Although animals show some environmental relationships, their distribution is not so restricted as plants. They are much more mobile than plants and, therefore, cannot be as precisely plotted. Neither are animals so markedly characteristic of, or limited to, certain geographic areas, so it is less easy to describe their distribution.

The distribution of the world's biotic resources oftentimes exerts a strong effect upon human economies. In climatic regions where grassland dominates the landscape, grazing may become the major occupation. In forested lands, man relies upon timber for shelter and the woodland animals for his food supply. When a significant ground cover is lacking, he seeks other sources of food and shelter. Modern man, however, is seldom satisfied with the biotic resources that nature provides. Rather, he seeks to improve them by introducing new species of plants and animals, by hybridization of plants and cross-breeding of animals, or by improvement in agrarian practices. Indeed, there are only a few parts of the earth where man has failed to alter the original biotic resources in a greater or lesser degree to satisfy his wants and needs better.

FORESTS

Although different tree species have varying environmental requirements because of physiological differences, there are certain species which are found associated with relatively extensive geographical areas. The distribution of tree species depends upon a number of factors among which are: (1) length of daylight and darkness, (2) temperature means and extremes, (3) length of growing season, (4) precipitation, (5) winds, (6) soil, and (7) drainage.

Forests are limited primarily to tropical rainforest, monsoon regions, humid subtropical, moister parts of humid continental, marine west coast, and subarctic climates. These climates meet tree requirements of adequate moisture, unfrozen subsoils during the growing season, and sufficiently long growing periods between killing frosts.

TROPICAL RAINFORESTS Many equatorial regions of Africa, South America and southeast Asia which receive heavy tropical rains that are well distributed and have relatively low elevations are characterized by tropical rainforests. Such rainforests are often known as *selvas*.

About one-tenth of the earth's surface, and nearly one-half of the earth's remaining forest area, is covered with tropical rainforests. Trees are tall, averaging more than 100 feet and occasionally exceeding 200 feet in height. Trees are closely spaced and interlaced with climbing vines called *lianas* and *epiphytes,* or air plants. The combined thick tree foliage, epiphytes, and woody lianas exclude sunlight from lower levels of the forest. Undergrowth is handicapped so that the ground surface is relatively clear. The forest is choked with underbrush in only a few specialized areas. Where light can penetrate to the forest floor as along a stream, on a steep slope, or at the edge of the forest, the region is an almost impenetrable wall of vegetation.

In tropical regions adjacent to coasts, mangrove thrives. Tidal flats, estuaries, and other areas of brackish water provide the ideal habitat for the stilt-root mangrove. Particularly large areas of mangrove swamp are to be found at the deltas of the great rivers of southeast Asia.

Tropical rainforests are composed of mixtures of thousands of tree species which include rich reserves of mahogany and teakwood and such tree products as camphor, quinine, gums, and rubber. It is difficult, if not impossible, to gauge their value because only a few of the thousands of tree species have been put to commercial use.

In contrast to the evergreen foliage canopy, the leaf litter of the forest floor is thin, and the soil is infertile. Decomposition of leaves is rapid and tree roots assimilate the products of decomposition almost as quickly as they are formed. Areas of tropical rainforests, when cleared, normally can support crops for only three or four years without heavy fertilization.

Most areas of tropical rainforest are uncleared, and sparsely inhabited by people. In those regions which are cleared for such crops as cassava, corn, bananas, rubber, coffee, and cacao, the soil is often quickly impoverished. Heavy convectional rains not only leach the soil but also erode it badly. As virgin forests are removed, the land is exposed to the full ravages of tropical downpours. Secondary growths of scrub forest often succeed the tropical rainforests.

Tropical rainforests are normally inhabited by a great variety of animals. Insects, fish, reptiles, and arboreal forms such as apes, birds, lizards, and monkeys are especially numerous. Most of the animals are relatively small except for the great apes, including the gorilla, and alligators, crocodiles, and the giant python snake. The rainforest literally teems with animal life. Most of the animals are adapted to life in the trees with apes, bats, birds, and monkeys, largely fruit eaters. Monkeys, of which there is a large variety of different species, occur in greatest numbers.

There is a scarcity of domesticated animals, such as cattle, horses, sheep, and swine, due in part to the scant human population and abundance of pestiferous insects. The climate is unfavorable, diseases kill many animals, and in some instances they cannot exist on the available forage. The water buffalo and the elephant are the primary beasts of burden in the rainforest.

MONSOON JUNGLES In northeastern India, Burma, Thailand, Cambodia, Laos, and Viet Nam, there is a distinct seasonal rhythm in the distribution of precipitation. Summers are characterized by heavy rains; winters are typically dry. Evergreen forests give way to semi-deciduous trees which lose their leaves during dry winter months. Many selva species are found in the monsoon forest, but they frequently drop their leaves in response to the seasonal rhythm of precipitation.

Trees are more widely spaced than in the tropical rainforest. Consequently, sunlight penetrates to the ground and a dense undergrowth develops. Such dense thickets of underbrush are termed *jungles*. Most of the trees do not retain their foliage during the dry season, but a few are evergreen. Areas of monsoon forests are generally easier to clear for crop production than other tropical forests, since a long dry season facilitates burning. Lumber is also easier to extract since pure stands of semi-deciduous trees are common. Tall bamboo thickets and tall grasses are encountered in certain regions thus lowering the yield of lumber per acre.

The native animal life includes mostly climbing, swimming, or flying species such as monkeys, reptiles, birds, and insects. The fauna common to the tropical jungles are closely related to the animal forms within the tropical rainforest. Since monsoon jungles may result from second growths after cutting, burning, and clearing of tropical rainforests, as well as in response to a specific climatic environment, few ground-dwelling animal species except reptiles are indigenous. Monsoon jungles seldom support large land-dwelling animals because of dense thickets of undergrowth. The high water table is an unfavorable habitat for most burrowing animals.

HUMID SUBTROPICAL FORESTS Humid subtropical trees are mostly coniferous species (needle-leaf trees), although broad-leaf evergreen, and deciduous species are not uncommon. For example, about ten species of pines compose most of the forests of the Atlantic and Gulf coastal plains of the United States. Pines are particularly dominant on poor, badly leached, sandy soils of the coastal plains. Well distributed precipitation, and a short cool season is favorable for tree growth. However, infertile, porous soils, and high evaporation rates lower the quality of the trees.

A lack of seasonal leaf fall, such as is characteristic of deciduous trees, dense undergrowth, and prevalence of climbing plants are typical of many humid subtropical forests. On cutover lands jungle-like thickets sometimes result. Bamboo thickets, for example, are common on the lowlands of China.

Mixed deciduous forests of excellent quality are found on certain sites where soil, slope, and climate are favorable. Remnants of such forests still exist, particularly within the humid subtropical portion of the United States.

The principal regions of humid subtropical forests are in the southeastern parts of the continents of North America, Asia, South America, Africa, and Australia. Forests in China, Japan, and Korea have been largely cleared and only poor remnants remain. In the southeastern part of the United States logging operations have been extensive, but wise reforestation programs have been carried out recently. Additional native forests remain in southern Brazil, Uruguay, southeastern Australia, and southeastern Africa. Most humid subtropical forests are relatively important lumber producing areas.

The animal life of the humid subtropical forest represents a transition from that of the tropical rainforest to the humid continental. Deer, bear, and fox are typical of the larger native animals. Squirrel, rabbit, opossum, raccoon, skunk, and porcupine are among the smaller animals. Alligators, turtles, and muskrats live in the swampy areas. Bright colored birds of many species inhabit the wooded regions. In humid subtropical climates of the southern hemisphere animal life is different and less abundant than in the northern hemisphere. Most notable are the woodland kangaroos of Australia, the short-horned buffalo of Natal in Africa, and the woodland deer and opossums in the Paraná Forests of South America.

HUMID CONTINENTAL MIXED FORESTS In humid continental climates most original native vegetation consists of deciduous broad-leaf trees. During winter, when freezing temperatures occur, the trees shed their relatively large leaves and enter a period of dormancy until spring. Today, most forests in humid continental climates are dominantly deciduous broad-leaf trees mixed with coniferous species. At the poleward margins of the deciduous forests coniferous species typical of the subarctic forest intermingle with broad-leaf varieties, and along the equatorward margin, pines of the subtropical forest are a significant part of the forest complex. Cutover lands are often planted to pine because of their rapid rate of growth.

The humid continental mixed forests normally require more than 30 inches of fairly well-distributed precipitation annually. Tree growth is limited by deficient rainfall and a high drought frequency. On the dry margins of the forests, grasses are typically dominant, and on the cold margins, coniferous forests succeed.

Humid continental forests are areas within which several tree associations exist. Oak, maple, beech, hickory, and elm are usually found in the United States. In the humid continental portions of Europe and Asia similar species are dominant, but their relationships to each other vary from place to place. The trees are normally not more than 100 feet in height, but this varies with species and location.

Much of the deciduous forest throughout the world has been cut to provide cropland. Forests remain principally on those rolling lands least suitable for agricultural crops. Conifers are normally cut for both lumber and pulpwood, whereas deciduous trees are used principally for plywood and lumber.

Animal life within mixed deciduous forests is essentially comparable with that within humid subtropical forests in terms of size and number of species. A long period of human settlement within the region has modified original species, but numerous wild small animals and insects still abound. Fish, along with migratory birds from subtropical regions, are also plentiful.

MARINE WEST COASTAL CONIFEROUS FORESTS The marine west coast region of North America supports magnificent coniferous forests. In the Pacific Northwest trees are frequently 200 to 300 feet high, with trunk diameters of 8 to 20 feet. Characteristic tree species are spruce, hemlock, redwood, Douglas fir, and sequoia. Several of these trees have a longevity of more than 1,000 years. Other marine west coasts have less striking forests, but northwestern Europe, New Zealand, and the southern coast of Chile are endowed with luxuriant trees.

Deciduous trees, which are neither so valuable nor so tall, are mixed with conifers in some parts of marine west coast climatic regions. Extensive areas of tall, rather slender conifers have been cleared in northwestern Europe, New Zealand, and the Pacific Northwest. Forests in southern Chile, which are still relatively inaccessible, remain mostly untouched by lumbering operations.

Animal species are varied in the marine west coast coniferous forests. A variety of arboreal forms, rodents, reptiles, browsing animals, and certain carnivores are commonly found. Animal life is still relatively abundant in most of these regions because of the thick forest cover. Fish, along with aquatic birds, are numerous in streams and along coastal areas. Elk, bear, wolf, fox, rabbit, and several varieties of deer are among the more important land animals.

THE TAIGA FORESTS The *taiga,* or northern coniferous forest, covers large areas in Alaska, northern Canada, the Scandinavian countries of Europe, and Siberia. The taiga consists primarily of pine, fir, spruce, and larch, although birch, poplar, willow, and ash are interspersed with the conifers. Permanently frozen subsoils prevent the growth of root systems and form the northern boundary of extensive conifers. Thin scrubby forests occupy the poleward margins of the taiga. Due to long, cold, dry winters, trees are normally small in size and growth is slow.

The taiga has recently become an important source of timber as well as a great producer of wood pulp. Lumbering is the chief economic activity of many areas of the taiga. Future lumbering prospects are somewhat dim, however. A very short period of sunlight, cold air, and poor soil provide a less than salubrious environment for tree growth.

The taiga is inhabited by a variety of animal forms. Rodents, fox, bear, deer, and wolves are generally abundant. Moose, deer, elk, and caribou are of considerable size, and in addition to these large herbivorous animals, small fur-bearing animals, such as the beaver, mink, otter, fox, and wolf are found. Insects, including flies and mosquitoes, are abundant. The taiga is the summer home of vast numbers of migratory birds, such as ducks, geese, herons, and many other varieties which find feeding grounds in the northern coniferous forests, and a favorable climate along with isolation which seems to meet their requirements.

GRASSLANDS

Grasslands are usually dominant where: (1) annual precipitation is low, (2) precipitation is unevenly or erratically distributed during the growing season, and (3) evaporation rates are generally high. *Tropical grasslands* usually prevail throughout areas with high evaporation rates and marked wet and dry seasons. *Midlatitude grasslands* are generally found in semiarid, drought-stricken areas. Soil types and soil moisture, in addition to rainfall, are factors governing the distribution of grasslands. Grasslands are the native vegetation of several soil types throughout the world. For example, compact, fine-textured and especially calcareous soils, such as chernozems, in humid areas usually support grasslands. Grasslands are often dominant where the upper soil areas are moist during much of the year, but the deeper soil layers are too dry for trees.

TROPICAL GRASSLANDS Tropical grasses predominate in areas between the wet tropical rainforest and dry steppes. The areas are usually covered with tall coarse-leafed grasses interspersed with scattered, stunted deciduous trees that often grow singly. In many places grasses are more than 6 to 8 feet tall during the wet season and wither into a tangled brown mat during the dry season.

Two main varieties of tropical grasslands should be noted. In the drier margins the native vegetation consists of typically short grasses and widely scattered bushes which grade into bush steppes.

On the equatorward side the open woodland of savanna grasses grade into tropical rainforests where more trees dominate the landscape. There are few .areas of tropical savanna grassland without some trees or shrubs interspersed. The trees are particularly prevalent along streams and in the better watered sections. Areas with scattered trees associated with grass are known as *park savannas*.

Savanna grasslands are the home of big game. A multitude of herbivorous forms, such as deer, antelope, gazelle, zebra, gnu, and water buffalo, take advantage of the available grass. In turn these herbivores are fed upon by large carnivores of the cat family, such as the lion, tiger, and leopard. Other herbivores, for example, the elephant, giraffe, and rhinoceros graze the grasses or browse the shrubs and trees undisturbed, because of their great size and strength.

INTERMEDIATE GRASSLANDS Intermediate grasslands lie at the dry edge of humid climates. The more luxuriant tall grasses may border humid climatic regions, whereas short grasses and bunch grasses typically occur in the drier areas. Tall, deep-rooted prairie grasses grow from 3 to 6 feet in height in the more humid areas. Shallow-rooted short grass steppes prevail in the more arid regions because of shallow depths of moist soil. Areas of more porous soils, high evaporation, or low rainfall (where less soil moisture is available) are likely to support bunch grass.

Some of the most fertile soils in the world have supported intermediate grasslands. Early settlements in grassland regions were retarded because of the lack of wood for fuel and building materials, the frequent occurrence of poor drainage, malaria, damage from prairie fires, and the difficulty of turning the tough sod with wooden or iron plows. In addition, these grassland regions were often inaccessible because of the general absence of navigable waterways. Today they are among the world's most productive agricultural areas, since the steel plow can turn over the tough soil and overland transportation is available.

Intermediate grasslands were once occupied by large numbers of grazing animals, such as bison (commonly called buffalo) and deer, but these animals have been generally replaced by domesticated types. Smaller animals, particularly of the rodent family, are still common in localities of intermediate grasslands. These animals are continuously trailed by carnivores, such as the wolf and coyote. The larger indigenous animals were fleet of foot, had great endurance, and roamed over extensive areas.

XEROPHYTIC SHRUB AREAS

An especially close relationship exists between xerophytic shrubs and environmental conditions. Plants which have survived are those which have developed an ability to live in areas of limited moisture. Moisture limitations may be due to slight precipitation, salty soil, excessive drainage, or because precipitation occurs in the form of snow, subsequently compacted into ice. Porous soils, steep valley walls, or salty soils may induce the development of xerophytic vegetation even in humid climates.

CHAPARRAL Scattered distributions of drought-resistant, dense, shrubby trees, found in dry subtropical climates, are variously known as *chaparral, maquis, macchia,* and *mallee.* Chaparral is generally confined to areas where temperatures do not exceed 100°F., and average annual precipitation is 10 to 35 inches. This shrubby vegetation is peculiarly equipped with thick bark and small, stiff, leathery leaves, which are sometimes densely covered with fine hairs that limit loss of moisture. Some bushes have thorns, which take over the function of leaves and further limit transpiration.

Wetter areas adjacent to chaparral are covered by sparse semi-xerophytic tree growth known as *schlerophyll forest.* Commercial products of the schlerophyll forest include olives, cork, and figs, but their more widespread economic importance normally lies in providing a protective cover against stream and wind erosion, and landslides. Many brush-land shrubs are resinous, burn easily, and often become fire hazards during the long dry summer season.

Semiarid environments, particularly the tropical steppes, frequently are covered by a sparse vegetation of thorny shrubs. Droughty soil conditions elsewhere caused by soil porosity, repeated burnings, or overgrazing may lead to the establishment of shrub forms.

The widespread distribution of shrub lands has led to the evolution of a variety of animal forms. In the semiarid lands of Asia, for example, large herbivorous animals, such as the Mongolian gazelle, antelope, and the two-humped camel, well suited to the harsh conditions, thrive. Carnivores, like the wolf, fox, coyote, and weasel are widely distributed in North America, the tiger in southwestern Asia, the lion in Africa, and the dingo in Australia. Rodents, including prairie dogs, rabbits, gophers, and reptiles, especially snakes and lizards, maintain themselves throughout these shrub areas.

DESERT PLANTS A desert is a region where the rate of evaporation exceeds precipitation. Most deserts support both flora and fauna but in limited degree. Desert plants are widely scattered with considerable barren ground between them. The deep tap roots of the mesquite or the widespread root systems of the evergreen creosote bush and their distinctively small but strong leaf and stem structures are direct responses to the lack of moisture.

Many xerophytic plants (plants which are adapted to little moisture supply) also develop thick bodies with pithy stems and small, thick leaves or leaves which have been modified to thorns. Cacti oftentimes have such extensive root systems that they can absorb enough water in a single thundershower to endure several months. They are also equipped with expansible stems that serve as excellent water storage tanks and are drawn upon as moisture is needed. Thick skins, shiny leaf surfaces, and silvered undersides of leaves are additional physical characteristics of certain desert plants.

Xerophytic plants are often spaced with amazing evenness over the desert. The uniform spacing is apparently correlated with available moisture: the less rainfall, the wider the spacing. Two prime factors control the abundance and distribution of desert plants: (1) the number of seeds which germinate, and (2) the growing conditions the seedlings encounter. Experiments have shown that a surprisingly high percentage of all desert seedlings which have sprouted after a heavy rain do survive, grow, and reproduce seeds.

Animal life in arid landscapes is quite varied, but members of the reptile, rodent, insect, and bird families seem to subsist best.

Small animals are the general rule. The desert fox is the largest indigenous animal of the Sahara.

Other true desert animals are the camel, the gazelle, and the hare. The sheep, goat, and donkey are all apparently native to desert climates and can adjust to a meager water supply and to coarse scanty forage. Some varieties of desert sheep have the ability to store fat on their hips and in their tails. The camel uses the fat in his hump as a built-in food supply for periods when food is particularly scarce.

Although all animals of the desert are well adjusted to the dry habitat, the camel best exemplifies adjustment to drought conditions. The camel's stomach can store water; his hump stores food by way of fat; his lips are equipped with tough skin for eating thorny xerophytic shrubs; the nostrils can be constricted to keep out sand and dust; large feet are padded to enable walking on loose, hot desert sand; and heavy hairs in his nose enable him to filter the dusty air he breathes.

TUNDRA VEGETATION The most important condition affecting plant life in the tundra is permafrost. Each summer the topsoil thaws and vegetation grows. The soil does not thaw sufficiently, however, to permit roots to develop at great depth. Consequently, sedges, lichens, and mosses are typical vegetative types. Vegetation of the tundra is especially adapted for a short growing season. Thus, it is generally stunted and compact with only lower forms prevailing. Most plants have the ability to sprout, grow, flower, and produce seed in a remarkably short time, in some instances a matter of a few weeks.

Nature has already eliminated most of the plant types that are unable to compete successfully in cold climates. A struggle for existence is not waged among the well-established forms, but new types are eliminated either because they germinate at inopportune times, or are less frost-resistant. It is the survival of the fit which accounts for few cold climate plants being killed by frost.

Because of great distances from densely peopled areas, tundra regions carry a surprising number of wild animals. Migratory birds by the millions nest in the muskeg regions of the tundra. Large grazing animals, like the caribou and musk ox are quite

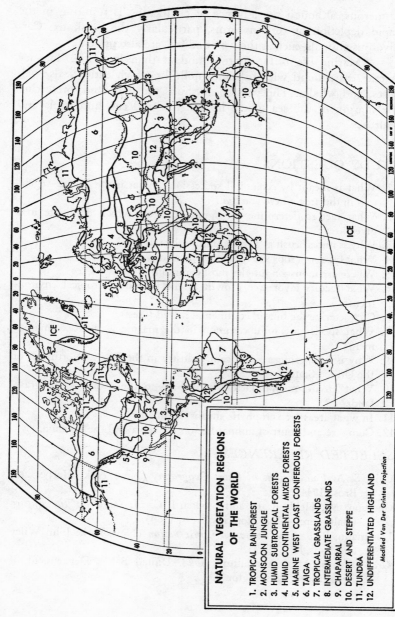

NATURAL VEGETATION REGIONS
OF THE WORLD

1. TROPICAL RAINFOREST
2. MONSOON JUNGLE
3. HUMID SUBTROPICAL FORESTS
4. HUMID CONTINENTAL MIXED FORESTS
5. MARINE WEST COAST CONIFEROUS FORESTS
6. TAIGA
7. TROPICAL GRASSLANDS
8. INTERMEDIATE GRASSLANDS
9. CHAPARRAL
10. DESERT AND STEPPE
11. TUNDRA
12. UNDIFFERENTIATED HIGHLAND

Modified Van Der Grinten Projection

Fig. 18 Natural vegetation regions of the world (highly generalized)

numerous, although the advance of civilization is resulting in the rapid depletion of certain forms, particularly the musk ox. Carnivorous animals, such as the wolf and fox, are also present.

Marine life is far more abundant than land life. The icy Arctic seas abound with fish and mollusks which entice seals, walruses, and whales. The polar bear shuns the mainland, preferring the margin of the sea where he can fish and can hunt seals and walruses.

STUDY QUESTIONS

1. What is meant by ecological succession? What is the climax vegetation in the area where you live?
2. What factors determine the species of trees which dominate in a given area?
3. Why is underbrush at a minimum in the selvas?
4. What types of crops are typical of the selvas?
5. Where are monsoon jungles most common?
6. What factors favor tree growth in the humid subtropical environment?
7. Characterize the humid continental mixed forests.
8. What species are most common in the marine west coast environment?
9. Why is lumbering a significant industry in the Pacific Northwest of the United States?
10. What environmental factors contribute to the evolution of grasslands?
11. In what areas are xerophytic shrubs dominant?
12. Compare and contrast animal life on the selva and the savanna.

SELECTED REFERENCES

Cain, S. A. *Foundations of Plant Geography* (New York: Harper and Bros., 1944).

Clawson, M., Held, R. B. and Stoddard, C. H. *Land for the Future* (Baltimore: Johns Hopkins Press, 1960).

Dassmann, R. F. *Environmental Conservation* (New York: John Wiley and Sons, Inc., 1959).

Grass. Yearbook of Agriculture, 1948, United States Department of Agriculture, Washington, D.C.

Huberty, M. R. and Flock, W. L. *Natural Resources* (New York: Mc-Graw-Hill Book Co., Inc., 1959).

James, P. E. and Jones, C. F. (editors), chapter by Küchler, A. W. "Plant Geography" in *American Geography: Inventory and Prospect* (Syracuse: Syracuse University Press, 1954), pp. 428-441.

Newbigin, M. I. *Plant and Animal Geography* (London: Methuen and Co., Ltd., 1936).

Trees. Yearbook of Agriculture, 1949, United States Department of Agriculture, Washington, D.C.

Weaver, J. E. and Clements, F. E. *Plant Ecology* (New York: McGraw-Hill Book Co., Inc., 2nd Edition, 1938).

Chapter Twelve ·

WATER RESOURCES

All life depends upon water. Water has a basic role in the formation of the protein molecule, the essential material for all plants and animals. In fact, our bodies are about 71 per cent water.

Water has been so widely and commonly distributed throughout most parts of the world that many people have been hardly aware that their very existence would be threatened if it were not present in sufficient quantities. On the other hand, those who live in the arid and semiarid climatic realms rightly place the highest value upon water. Residents of the humid lands are frequently so accustomed to finding water when and where they need it that they overlook its true importance.

USES OF WATER

The world's use of water has increased enormously. This is not only due to increasing population but also higher standards of cleanliness, better living, and rapid industrial expansion. The per capita use of water in the United States today has increased from about 500 gallons a day in 1900 to about 1,600 gallons. This includes all uses except recreation and hydroelectric power generation.

Water supplies are more essential than we consider them to be until we analyze their many uses. Several of the most important uses for water are: *domestic and municipal supplies, industrial processing, crop irrigation, abundant and dependable power, outdoor recreation,* and *waste disposal.*

DOMESTIC AND MUNICIPAL SUPPLIES There is enough water over all the earth for man's needs, but it is poorly distributed. Since about one-half of the world's population lives on less than one-twentieth of the land area, water supplies in densely populated areas often are inadequate. Water carrying still ranks as a time-consuming burden in many regions. Where water is carried great distances, it must be carefully conserved.

Not only are the world's needs for domestic water erratically distributed, but so is the world's water supply. That part of the United States east of the 100th meridian and a section of the Pacific Northwest have the most abundant water supplies. Between these two large areas are states with sparse water supplies. The per capita use of domestic and municipal water varies widely from one community to another, but it generally ranges from 60 gallons a day in towns of 500 population to 150 gallons or above in cities of 100,000 or more persons.

Since rural water comes from private sources, there is no record of the amount used in farm homes. The daily quantity estimated by the Soil Conservation Service, however, is 50 gallons per person, 15 gallons per cow, 4 gallons per hog, and 3 gallons per sheep and goat. The United States receives an average of about 4.8 billion acre-feet of water a year by precipitation of which about 1.4 billion acre-feet becomes runoff. Our present annual rate of consumption is about one-seventh the annual runoff. Thus, despite uneven geographical distribution of precipitation and consumption, we have a natural margin to work with in the future.

Industrial Uses Water is industry's prime raw material. Since 1900 United States' industrial production has risen by more than 700 per cent. More than half of the gain has been achieved within the last ten years. In terms of water needs, economic or industrial activities consume more than domestic uses. Approximately 1,400 gallons of water are necessary for the production of a dollar's worth of steel and nearly 2,000 for a dollar's worth of paper. The weaving of one yard of woolen cloth requires about 500 gallons. In 1960, United States' industry used about 150 billion tons of water which was about 50 times the weight of all other industrial materials.

Vast amounts of water are used for cooling or processing purposes especially in such industries as iron and steel, synthetic rubber, explosives, food and beverage, pulp and paper, and meat packing. However, about 65 per cent of industrial water is used by electric power plants where the water is transformed into steam or used for condenser cooling. The other 35 per cent is used mainly for manufacturing or processing.

Large water-using industries normally are located in cities which have abundant water supplies. Lake cities, such as Milwaukee, Chicago, and Toledo are preferred by industries which require great quantities of fresh water. The trend is toward more highly refined products which normally need increased water supplies.

CROP IRRIGATION Crop irrigation is the greatest consumptive use of water in the United States. Irrigation has brought a great variety of crops into areas which formerly seemed sterile. Without irrigation, millions of acres of land would produce nothing. Irrigation uses 5 times as much water as municipalities and uses 3 times as much water as all other uses combined in the United States.

Because soils in arid regions have not been leached, they contain much plant food. Some early civilizations, such as those in Iraq and Egypt, developed along irrigated river valleys. Today irrigation waters for crop production are taken from diverse sources such as rivers, creeks, lakes, storage basins, and from underground sources.

India has more irrigated land than any other country of the world. Large areas along the upper Ganges and Indus rivers are watered by irrigation. In addition, water from wells and storage tanks is spread over land by human or animal labor. In Iraq the flood plains of the Tigris and Euphrates rivers are irrigated by water from adjacent streams. Within the United States about 30,000,000 acres of land are irrigated. About 12 per cent of all United States cropland is so watered with an average of 40 billion gallons a day. The worth of the crops harvested from irrigated lands in the United States is about one-third the total crop value. Much water in irrigated regions is lost through wasteful agricultural practices, seepage, or evaporation.

WATER POWER Regions which use water as a source of power require a number of favorable geographic conditions. They include: (1) abundant precipitation; (2) uniform stream flow; (3) a slope or gradient sufficient to give relatively high stream velocities; and (4) nearness to market. An ideal situation is found at Niagara Falls, where fairly well-distributed rainfall over a large drainage basin has its volume regulated by numerous lakes, and finally tumbles over a cliff about 160 feet high. In addition, Niagara Falls is located near a large consuming market for electric power.

These geographic factors have been placed under "push-button" control by man. Engineers have placed concrete ledges above the falls to secure an even flow of water. Turbines, dynamos, generators, inter-connected power plants, and high-tension transmission provide abundant electrical energy to nearby markets. Water-power projects usually serve many functions concomitantly. In some areas irrigation, flood control, navigation, recreation resorts, and improved land use may all be derived from the same water source.

Much of the world's potential water power is located in undeveloped areas of Africa, Asia, and South America where heavy well-distributed rainfall occurs at high elevations. Most of the world's developed water power is located in the United States, Norway, Switzerland, Sweden, Italy, Germany, Canada, and Japan where man has established a need for power, and has also acquired the skill and capital necessary for its use.

More water is withdrawn from streams and reservoirs to generate power than for all other uses combined. An average of 1,500 billion gallons a day was withdrawn for water-power in 1955, more than 7 times as much as for all other purposes in the United States. But practically all this water is returned to the streams. Usually its quality is not changed, except for an increase in temperature. This use ordinarily does not materially reduce the supply of water for other purposes since the water is not consumed.

SCENIC AND RECREATIONAL FACILITIES Numerous amusement centers, resorts, and picnic areas throughout the world owe their attractiveness to water. The recreational industry is growing as more leisure time becomes available to more people. Since people often prefer water sites for relaxation, more water areas will undoubtedly be developed for recreational purposes. The use of streams or lakes for vacation or holiday excursions depends largely upon the condition of the watershed (drainage basin) of which they are a part. For example, the productivity of fishing waters reflects the general fertility of the watersheds from which they drain. Loss of fertility through clean-cutting of forests, fire, and destructive farming practices, reduces fish population. Flooding, silting, and pollution of streams by excessive erosion along with the discharge of industrial and domestic wastes into streams and lakes have further reduced their scenic and recreational value.

Good conditions can be restored by wise watershed and flood management programs. Recreational opportunities can be increased through the construction of artificial bodies of water and through the purification of polluted streams. Generally the above measures not only serve to provide improved swimming, boating, camping, and picknicking, but to control floods, promote wildlife, and to provide water for stock.

Water is neither withdrawn nor consumed when used for recreation, although some is lost by evaporation and seepage. But the withdrawal and consumptive uses, such as irrigation and industry, often reduce the supply or diminish the value of water for recreation and wildlife.

Waste Disposal In 1950, 11,800 United States municipal sewer systems and 10,400 independent factory-waste outlets were discharging into public waters. Only 6,700 of the sewage plants and 2,600 of the industrial plants gave adequate treatment to the wastes. More than 2,000 industries discharged inorganic wastes, such as acids and poisonous chemicals. In addition, drainage from abandoned coal mines daily poured 10,000 tons of acid pollution into waterways within the United States. Although cities and industries return nearly 90 per cent of the water they use to natural sources, some of the water may be largely worthless for reuse.

Stream flows once were adequate to handle the nation's untreated wastes without significant damage to other water users. As the population grew, we had to turn to the septic tank, then to primary treatment and finally to complete treatment, often with chlorination.

Water pollution comes chiefly from two sources: human sewage and industrial waste. The problem of waste disposal is increasing because we have more sewage and more industrial wastes but less water available to carry them away. There is less good water available to carry away wastes because, as our population, cities, and industries grow, our demands increase for water for other uses.

SOURCES OF WATER

The sea is the source of our water supply. The "water cycle," from oceans to the atmosphere, from the atmosphere in the form of precipitation, and back to the sea, constantly renews the water supply. As water falls upon the ground, some runs off over the surface, some is held in the soil, and some percolates to ground water. Surface runoff and ground water supply direct human needs in homes, industries, irrigation, and recreation. Nationwide, about 80 per cent comes from surface sources and 20 per cent from ground water.

SURFACE WATER

Precipitation is not spread evenly over the country. It ranges from 120 inches a year along the western slopes of the Olympic Peninsula of the Pacific Northwest to less than 5 inches in the arid Southwest. Within a region, the water that falls is divided into separate portions by watersheds. A watershed is any area of land that drains into a particular stream or body of water.

Surface water is the major source of available water. It supplies about 75 per cent of the water used by cities and towns and by farmers for irrigation, 90 per cent of the fresh water used by industry, and nearly all of that used for hydroelectric power in the United States.

If the water drains too rapidly, it cuts gullies and carries off topsoil. The soil and debris which the water carries into streams reduce the amount of water the stream or lake can hold and thus decrease the available water supply. Such sediment carried downstream by runaway water may greatly increase the cost of cleaning and filtering the water for municipal uses. It can interfere with the hydroelectric plant which produces electricity.

When water runs away too rapidly, it may cause a flood which damages farms, ranches, crops, property, homes, highways, and utilities. Choking of stream channels with sediment makes floods more serious because the clogged-up stream bed can carry less water. Sediment deposited in reservoirs after heavy rains also reduces the amount of water that can be stored for use in water-short areas. But water can be slowed down and used to better advantage when proper soil and water conservation methods and other flood-prevention measures are put into effect all over a watershed. Terraces, stripcropping, more grass and legumes in crop rotations, improved pastures, and other practices make more water soak into the ground.

GROUND WATER

Precipitation that does not evaporate or drain off into streams sinks into the ground. That portion of the water which sinks into the ground provides *ground water*. Although the soil may be dry for a few inches or a few feet below the surface, it is common in quarries, mines or wells to find the rock thoroughly saturated with water at comparatively shallow depths. The upper limit of the zone of saturation is known as the *water table*.

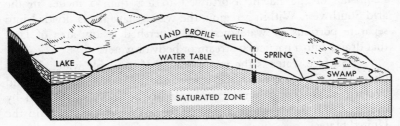

Fig. 19   Relationship between water table, wells, lakes, and swamps

WATER TABLE The water table is an irregular surface which tends to conform somewhat to surface configuration. Normally it is higher beneath hills than beneath lowlands, although usually nearer the surface beneath the latter. It coincides with the earth's surface at the seashore, in swampy places, and along banks of permanent streams. It is above the surface of the ground where permanent ponds or lakes occur.

Water tables rise and fall with changes in amounts of precipitation. Ordinarily at any locality the water table is higher during wet weather than during long dry periods. It is customary to use the term, water table, to indicate the average position of the top of the zone of saturation throughout a considerable period of time.

MOVEMENT There are two main forces which cause movement of ground water; gravity and capillary action. *Capillary action* tends to draw water into exceedingly small tube-like openings, regardless of the direction of movement, be it upward, downward, or sideward. *Gravity* causes water to "seek its own level" underground precisely as it does above ground. Hence, movement under gravity is ordinarily downward.

All openings underground may be regarded as pores, for even the largest cavern is no more than a pore in comparison with the size of the earth. The ability of rock material to hold and yield water is determined largely by the characteristics of those pores. This quality is called *porosity*. Water-bearing beds are known as *aquifers*.

POROSITY The porosity of loose rock materials varies with the arrangement, shape, and degree of assortment of the particles. The size of the grain is not a determining factor, because if other conditions are the same, a material will have the same porosity whether it consists of large or small grains. Silt or clay, consisting entirely of minute particles, may have a porosity as great as coarse gravel, although the pores are less easily seen. The original porosity of certain rocks has been reduced by compaction. In others it has been increased by development of fractures or by dissolving some rock material.

Rocks of low porosity are necessarily limited in their capacity to absorb, hold, or yield water. In general, the porosity of rocks tends to be higher near the surface and lower with increasing depth. The least porous rocks are those that are buried so deeply that the weight upon them is sufficiently great to reduce pores to microscopic size.

The depth at which pressures are great enough to force closure of pores is believed to be about 20 to 30 miles. The top of the zone of rock flowage is the theoretical lower limit to which ground water will penetrate. Water has been obtained from rocks at depths of more than 2 miles, but in most places deep wells yield little water below a depth of half a mile. All rock is said to contain some water but not always in productive amounts.

PERMEABILITY The rate of movement of water beneath the surface depends upon the capacity of the rock material for transmitting water. Ground water may move laterally and ultimately to the oceans or to places where the water is discharged at the land surface as in springs or seeps. In the pumping of ground water with the aid of wells a hole is drilled into the zone of saturation. As that water is pumped out, other water moves toward the well. The rate at which water moves toward the well, and therefore the rate at which water can be withdrawn from the well, depends largely on the *permeability* (flowage ability) of the materials from which the water is drawn. In rocks of low permeability water is practically stagnant. Rocks which are highly permeable permit rapid flow of water into and from their pores. Rocks which are comparatively impermeable deflect or prevent circulation of ground water. Many hillside springs, for example, are located along the plane of contact of porous or permeable rock material with an underlying nonporous or impermeable horizon.

Ground water, where concentrated in underground streams, may do considerable mechanical work. However, this is small when compared with the chemical work accomplished. Chemically, ground water acts as both a solvent and precipitant. It also aids the atmosphere in weathering earth's materials by hydration, oxidation, and carbonation.

Results of ground water activity are conspicuous where limestone, which is readily dissolved by water containing carbon dioxide, is the common bedrock. Solution of limestone rock may cause the formation of underground caves and sink holes. Sink holes may develop at the surface by enlargements of openings through which water enters the ground, or they may result from the collapse of a portion of the roof of a cavern. Sink holes are commonly less than 100 feet deep and only a few hundred feet in diameter. They can generally be distinguished by their circular shape and by pools of water often present in them. Topography characterized by solution sinks is called *karst*. Karst topography exhibits different characteristics as it develops. In the youthful stage it is characterized by only a few tiny sinks, and most drainage is at the surface. As solution progresses the sinks are greatly enlarged, caves and caverns are numerous, and most drainage is by underground means. This mature stage is succeeded by an old age stage where only a few residual limestone hills, called *mogotes,* are left standing above an erosional surface, and drainage has re-established itself on the surface at a lower elevation.

Ground water sources contain more water than all surface reservoirs and lakes combined, including the Great Lakes. Ground water is estimated to equal 10 years' average rainfall or 35 years' average runoff. Most ground water is part of the water cycle.

Under certain conditions water is held under hydrostatic pressure on dipping structures known as *artesian* structures.

PROBLEMS

In many areas ground water is being used faster than it is naturally replenished. In effect, the stored water is being "mined"; water levels in wells are dropping, and the irrigation projects, municipalities, and industries depending on them are threatened.

United States water shortages are commonplace. Many of the most critical water problems of the United States are created by our increasing tendency to concentrate in dense settlements. The United States is becoming more urbanized, and water in sufficient quantities to serve cities of hundreds of thousands or of millions usually cannot be found in the immediate vicinity of such settlements. The drier regions have a more serious problem of finding an adequate urban supply, but cities in humid sections of the country also have their water shortages.

Los Angeles has to transport some of its water 250 miles. Denver will have to cross a mountain range to get enough water. A number of cities on the Great Plains and in the Southwest have serious or crippling water supplies. Some, like Wichita, Kansas, or Dallas, Texas, have real engineering problems as to where they can turn in a dry environment for the large additional water supplies needed. The New York metropolitan area had first to tap the streams of the Catskills, and then the Delaware River, 70 miles away. Boston, Massachusetts, solved its problem only with a 70-mile aqueduct that carries water from central Massachusetts to that metropolitan area. In all, the United States Geological Survey reported that in 1953 about one-third of the 200 cities in the United States above 50,000 population were suffering from inadequate water supplies. One-fourth of all the people served by public water supplies had their service curtailed in the summer of 1953, which was an abnormally dry summer.

Several disastrous floods occur over the earth's surface annually which often directly affect millions of persons. In the United States alone the total annual loss from floods is estimated at more than one billion dollars. Damage to crops, buildings, roads, and drainage facilities, stream bank erosion, gullying, and loss of life are but a few examples of direct flood losses. There is also great inconvenience to many persons indirectly affected.

Both physical and human factors contribute to flood conditions. Among the physical factors are amount and distribution of precipitation, slope of the land, vegetation, soil, and bedrock characteristics. These physical factors are not easily changed. But human practices which contribute to flooding can usually be improved. Numerous measures can be taken to conserve vegetation, soil, and water by increasing the rate at which soil absorbs water, and improving the latter's storage capacity. Such measures as crop rotation, strip cropping, cover crops, and reforestation reduce the rate and intensity of runoff. Flood-control devices such as levees, dams, and walls hold back flood water, but they are remedial measures rather than preventive devices. Floods can best be prevented by a watershed protection program, which promotes wise land use.

Serious problems of ground water shortages and salt water seepages occur in areas where water is pumped out faster than the entire ground water reservoir is replenished. Under these conditions the reservoir is emptied of water that may have taken decades or centuries to accumulate, and there is no possibility of a continuous perennial water supply unless these conditions are changed. Even more serious is the situation in which salty or otherwise unusable water flows into a ground water reservoir as the good water is pumped out. In such cases the reservoirs are ruined before they are emptied. Most of the excessively pumped reservoirs are in arid regions, where precipitation is generally inadequate for the needs of man. However, such humid areas as the Gulf Coast of Louisiana and the New England seaboard also have salt water encroachment problems following heavy use of ground water for irrigational or industrial purposes.

Overgrazing, poor land utilization, and unwise deforestation are major causes of water problems. Excessive uses of water have caused critical problems in many places. Serious deficiencies have become obvious in numerous areas. Steps must be taken to use water more wisely in the future as population and per capita needs increase at an alarming rate. Our underground water supplies can be preserved best by reducing water runoff, curtailing waste, controlling natural losses, and artificially recharging of ground water supplies by increasing the number of lakes and dams.

STUDY QUESTIONS

1. List and discuss the major uses of water.
2. What is the source of the municipal water supply for your city?
3. Why is water so significant for industry?
4. Where are the great areas of irrigated land?
5. What is meant by the water table?
6. How does water move through the soil?
7. What creates the major water problems of flooding, lowering water table, etc.?
8. In what ways may the water supply be conserved?
9. Enumerate and project solutions for some of the major water problems.
10. What kinds of users would be primarily dependent upon ground water? On surface water?

SELECTED REFERENCES

Carrier, E. H. *The Thirsty Earth: A Study in Irrigation* (London: Christophers, 1928).

Chauvin, R. S. "The World's Waters" in Miller, E. W. and Renner, G. T. and associates. *Global Geography* (New York: Thomas Y. Crowell Co., 2nd Edition, 1957), pp. 79-94.

Dohrs, F. E., Sommers, L. M. and Petterson, D. R. *Outside Readings in Geography* (New York: Thomas Y. Crowell Co., 1955), pp. 383-410.

Smith, G. H. (editor), *Conservation of Natural Resources* (New York: John Wiley and Sons, Inc., 1958).

Thomas, H. E. *The Conservation of Ground Water* (New York: McGraw-Hill Book Co., Inc., 1951).

Water. Yearbook of Agriculture, 1955, United States Department of Agriculture, Washington, D.C.

Chapter Thirteen

THE HYDROSPHERE

Only 29 per cent of the earth's surface is above sea level. If all the land were deposited in the sea, only 1/18th of the total volume of water would be displaced. If the earth's crust were ironed out and reduced to a perfect sphere, the hydrosphere (the earth's waters) would then completely submerge the land to a depth of about 8,000 feet.

IMPORTANCE

Ocean water plays an indispensable role in supporting life. The great ocean basins hold about 300 million cubic miles of water. From this vast amount, about 80,000 cubic miles of water are sucked into the atmosphere each year by evaporation and returned by precipitation and drainage to the ocean. More than 24,000 cubic miles of rain descends annually upon the continents. This vast amount is required to replenish the lakes and streams, springs and water tables on which all flora and fauna are dependent. Thus, the hydrosphere permits organic existence.

The hydrosphere has strange characteristics because water has properties unlike those of any other liquid. One anomaly is that water upon freezing expands by about 9 per cent, whereas most liquids contract on cooling. For this reason, ice floats on water bodies instead of sinking to the bottom. If the ice sank the hydrosphere would soon be frozen solidly, except for a thin layer of surface melt water during the summer season. Thus, all aquatic life would be destroyed and the interchange of warm and cold currents, which moderates climates, would be notably absent.

Another outstanding characteristic of water is that water has a heat capacity which is the highest of all liquids and solids except ammonia. This characteristic enables the oceans to absorb and store vast quantities of heat, thereby often preventing climatic extremes. In addition, water dissolves more substances than any other liquid. It is this characteristic which helps make oceans a great storehouse for minerals which have been washed down from the continents. In several areas of the world these minerals are being commercially exploited. Solar evaporation of salt is widely practiced, potash is extracted from the Dead Sea, and magnesium is produced from sea water along the American Gulf Coast.

WATER CYCLE

The water cycle (hydrologic cycle) consists of the circulation of the earth's moisture from the parent body of water into the atmosphere and return. We can think of water first evaporating from the hydrosphere, which covers about 71 per cent of the earth. After the moisture is lifted into the atmosphere, it eventually condenses and falls back to the surface of the earth as precipitation. Of the moisture which soaks into the ground, some is available for growing plants, and some is evaporated. The remainder reaches the deeper zones, slowly percolating via springs and seeps to maintain streams. The streams, in turn, eventually drain into the oceans where the water started, thus completing the cycle.

FEATURES

The mystery that formerly enshrouded the surface dimensions of the seas has been dispelled. Ocean travel is common today. Nevertheless, complete knowledge of the depths of the ocean has not yet been achieved. Very little was known of ocean depths prior to 1920. At that time sonic soundings, a method for measuring depth by timing the interval required for a sound impulse to travel to the ocean floor and back, was developed.

Today, the study of the geography of ocean basins is taking form, and it is now possible to visualize sections of the earth which are covered by the sea. Although ocean basins differ from one another topographically as much as continents, they share certain common features. One such feature is that each ocean can be divided into three parts: (1) *continental shelves,* (2) *continental slopes,* and (3) *their floors.*

CONTINENTAL SHELF The continental shelves are the submerged edges of the continents. During past ages they have been alternately flooded and exposed with the rise and fall of sea level. From most continents, the bottom of the sea descends gradually to a depth of about 600 feet. It then plunges abruptly to the ocean floor. The shelf extends outward from the continents for distances of 10 to 800 miles. The latter figure is representative of the shelf which stretches northward 800 miles from the Soviet Union into the Arctic Ocean.

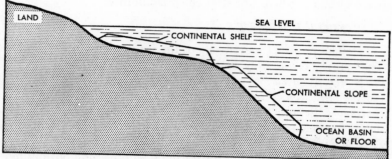

Fig. 20   Relationship between continental shelf, continental slope, ocean basin or floor, and the land

CONTINENTAL SLOPES Off mountainous coasts, the continental slope may descend to the ocean floor more precipitously than do the walls of the Grand Canyon to the bottom of the gorge. In a few areas the drop is as much as 30,000 feet in a single plunge.

OCEAN FLOOR At the base of the continental slopes lies the deep ocean floor. It comprises about one-half of the total area of the earth. In a sense the term *floor* is misleading, for only in certain places is the deep sea bottom flat. Most of the ocean beds are ribbed and corrugated. Each ocean has its *deeps* (troughs of great depth), each with its own physical characteristics. Curiously, the ocean deeps usually appear along the edges of islands rather than being isolated in mid-ocean. The deepest known trench is the Mariana Trench in the Pacific Ocean where man has descended in a bathyscape to more than 38,000 feet.

The ocean floor is far from smooth. Huge submerged mountain ranges give variety to the ocean floor. The Mid-Atlantic Ridge, for example, has an occasional peak, which projects above the surface to form an island such as Ascension and the Azores. Submarine canyons of unkown origin crease the ocean floor, and curious flat-topped submerged mountains, called *guyots* project above it. Coral polyps have built reefs and produced *atolls,* of which some are submerged and others project above the water. Oceanographers have barely scratched the surface of knowledge to be learned about the ocean's waters, its floor, and its peculiar landforms.

MOVEMENTS

The principal movements of the sea result from five factors. They are: (1) *the drag of the prevailing winds;* (2) *differences in the density of various sea waters;* (3) *the rotation of the earth;* (4) *the attraction of the moon and sun;* and (5) *the shape of the continents.* Because water is a liquid, the oceans are in a constant state of motion. Three major movements result from the five above-mentioned causes, namely, *waves, tides,* and *currents.*

WAVES The waves of the ocean present the most obvious motion. However, they affect merely the surface layers. Ordinary waves are due to the drag of winds upon the water which sets up a rhythmic, up-and-down motion. Occasionally the surface of the hydrosphere appears smooth and glassy, but normally it is characterized by some undulations.

TIDES Tides differ from waves in that they are more regular, and move whole masses of water. Whereas waves are caused by wind and weather, tides are produced by the moon and sun. The rise and fall of the tides at any place varies in accordance with the position of the moon and sun.

Twice each day at most places the level of the hydrosphere in any given area rises and falls. The reason for two tides daily is the changing relative strength of the moon's gravitational pull upon: (1) the waters of the earth nearest the moon, (2) the solid part of the earth, and (3) the waters of the earth opposite the moon. The water nearest the moon is pulled to a high tide. The solid part of the earth is less affected by the gravitational pull, but more strongly affected than the waters of the earth opposite the moon. The latter lag behind and cause another high tide in that area.

When the moon, sun, and earth are in line, as during periods of the new and full moon extraordinarily high tides, called *spring tides* are created. During the first and third quarter phase of the moon, when the gravitational attractions of the sun and moon are acting at right angles, quite low tides, called *neap tides,* are experienced.

Many factors other than the gravitational attraction of celestial bodies have a bearing on the character of tides. Some of these include the depth of the ocean basin, the configuration of the coastline and of the ocean basin. Indentations or embayments normally experience greatest tidal fluctuations. The Bay of Fundy in Nova Scotia, for example, has a range from high to low water of more than 50 feet.

OCEAN CURRENTS The rotation of the earth causes both wind and ocean currents to be deflected to the right in the northern hemisphere and to the left in the southern hemisphere. Thus in the northern hemisphere the waters move clockwise, and in the southern hemisphere counterclockwise. Just as there is a pattern in the world's wind system, so the oceans have a definite circulating pattern. The frictional effect of the winds moving over the surface of ocean waters causes a relatively thin layer of top water to move slowly in the direction of the winds. Other causes for ocean currents are differences in density due to variation in temperature, evaporation, and salinity. The 28°F. sea water temperature of the Arctic is in sharp contrast to the steamy heat of the Red Sea where waters may be as warm as 90°F. Obviously, too, the salinity of water in a sea such as the Red Sea which is surrounded by deserts, is much greater than a sea in humid regions, such as the Baltic Sea.

THE OUTLOOK

Within the near future the ocean may become our largest and most important resource. Extraction of copper, boron, and vanadium from the hydrosphere will probably soon be profitable. Magnesium, salt, and potash are already being commercially recovered in large quantities. These extractions yield water acceptable, even as drinking water, as a by-product. Apparently the main limiting factors for the future are demand and technology.

If and when fresh water can be derived from sea water at a cost that compares favorably with current fresh water rates, significant changes will be brought about. For example, if the water supply of Los Angeles, which is now brought in from the Colorado River were to come from the Pacific Ocean, water from the Colorado River would be available for use in irrigating desert lands in Nevada, Arizona, and southeastern California; and the people of Los Angeles would enjoy more abundant, dependable, and cheaper water supply. This alone would open up several million acres for increased agricultural production.

STUDY QUESTIONS

1. What percentage of the earth's surface is above sea level?
2. What are some peculiar physical characteristics of water as a liquid? Why are these characteristics significant to geographers?
3. What is meant by the hydrologic cycle?
4. Distinguish between continental shelf, continental slope, and ocean floor.
5. What five principal factors cause the movement of the waters in the sea?
6. Explain what is meant by a neap tide? By a spring tide?
7. What causes ocean currents? What is their pattern of movement?
8. In what way is the ocean of value to man now? How may it become valuable in the future?

SELECTED REFERENCES

Carson, R. L. *The Sea Around Us* (London: Oxford University Press, 1951).

Coker, R. E. *This Great and Wide Sea* (Chapel Hill: The University of North Carolina Press, 1947).

Sverdrup, H. V. *Oceanography for Meteorologists* (New York: Prentice-Hall Inc., 1942).

Sverdrup, H. V., Johnson, M. W. and Fleming, R. H. *The Oceans: Their Physics, Chemistry and General Biology* (New York: Prentice-Hall, Inc., 1942).

APPENDIX

APPENDIX A

LAND SURVEY SYSTEMS

Property must be delimited in definite terms to insure the rights of the owner and to avoid interminable legal difficulties. As the United States was first settled by Europeans a system of land survey called "metes and bounds" was employed. This system of location is still used extensively in many parts of the world, although its shortcomings, which will be described subsequently, are numerous. This method employs the use of natural features of the landscape, such as trees, rocks, streams, etc. and distances and directions from these reference points. From the standpoint of future litigation it is unfortunate that trees die, rocks are moved, and compass needles vary in direction from year to year. The division of land which results from the use of such a pattern is extremely irregular and makes for great difficulty in road construction, agriculture, and other human pursuits.

Fortunately as the lands north and west of the Ohio River became part of the public domain, a new system was adopted by Congress. The plan as written into law provided that "the surveyor . . . shall proceed to divide the said territory into townships of six miles square, by lines running due north and south, and others crossing these at right angles, as near as may be." The evolution of this system has resulted in a series of townships numbered east and west of a given principal meridian and north and south of a specific base line. Each township, which is approximately six miles on a side contains about 36 square miles, or sections. Each section contains 640 acres. Each section may be further subdivided for the purposes of description. Because meridians converge it is necessary to compensate for this convergence by surveying a new standard parallel every fourth tier of townships north of the base

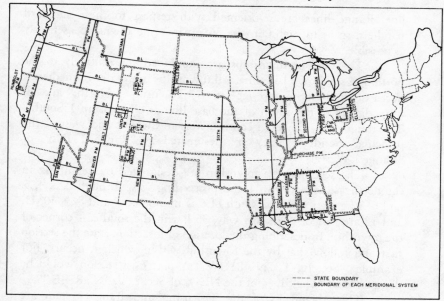

Fig. 21   *United States land survey*

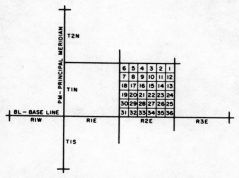

Fig. 22   *Relationship of Township to Base Line and Range Line*

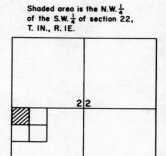

Fig. 23   *Portions of a Section*

line. Range lines are re-oriented with respect to these standard parallels, so as to maintain the 36 square mile township as nearly as possible.

The tiers of townships are numbered consecutively to the north and south of a base line. All townships in the tier immediately north of the base line are labeled as "Township 1 North," and all immediately to the south of the base line as "Township 1 South." The ranges are numbered consecutively to the east and west of the principal meridian. They are designated as "Range 1 East" or "Range 1 West."

The sections of a township are designated by beginning in the northeast corner with 1 and proceeding west through 2, 3, 4, 5, and 6. The section to the south of 6 is numbered 7 and 8, 9, 10, 11, and 12 are east of 6. In this way, 36 lies in the southeast corner of the township. In describing the location of a section, state the section first and follow that by the township within which it occurs. For example: "Sec. 10, T. 2N., R. 4W." A part of a section would be designated as "The SE ¼ of the NE ¼ of Sec. 2, T. 3N., R. 4E."

The advantages of the Township and Range system are numerous. Land descriptions are simplified, the boundaries of sections are usually marked by roads, which produces a rectangular grid pattern, and boundaries of properties are firmly established.

A BRIEF SYNOPSIS OF
TREWARTHA-KOEPPEN
CLASSIFICATION OF CLIMATE

A—Humid tropical climates .... Average temp. of coldest month over 64.4°

    Af—*tropical rainforest* ..... 2.4" precipitation or more each month

    Aw—*savanna* .... At least 1 mo. less than 2.4"

    Am—*monsoon* .... Large annual total precipitation; short dry period

B—Dry climates—evaporation rate is high (r = 0.44t — 8.5)*

    BW—*desert* .... W—if annual ppn. is less than r/2

        BWh—*low lat. desert* .. h—coldest mo. over 32°

        BWk—*mid. lat. desert* k—coldest mo. below 32°

    BS—*steppe* .... S—if annual ppn. exceeds r/2

        BSh—*low latitude*

           steppe .... h—see above

        BSk—*mid. lat. steppe* .. k—see above

C—Humid mesothermal .... coldest month between 64.4° and 32°

    Cs—dry summer (*Mediterranean*) .... s—one summer month has under 1.2"; wettest winter mo. 3 times driest summer month

        Csa—hot summer ..... a—warmest month over 71.6°

        Csb—cool summer .... b—warmest month under 71.6°

---

* NOTE: For summer ppn. concentration, use r = 0.44t — 3.5
    For winter ppn. concentration, use r = 0.44t — 14

Ca—*humid subtropical*

Caw .... w—wettest summer month has 10 times ppn. of driest winter month

Caf .... f—no dry season, i.e., neither s nor w

Cb—*marine west coast* ..... b—warmest month below 71.6°

Cc—*marine west coast* ..... c—only 1 to 3 months over 50°

D—Humid microthermal .... coolest month is below 32°, warmest above 50°

Da—*humid continental, long summer* .... a—see above

Daf .... f—see above

Daw .... w—see above

Db—*humid continental, short summer* .... b—see above

Dbf .... f—see above

Dbw .... w—see above

Dc & Dd—*subarctic* or *taiga*

Dcf .... c & f—see above

Dcw .... c & w—see above

Ddw .... w—see above d—coldest month below —36.4°

E—Polar Climates .... warmest month under 50°

ET—*Tundra* .... T—one or more months below 50° but over 32°

EF—*Ice Cap* .... F—warmest month below 32°

---

i = temp. range less than 9°F. (A or B climates)

n = fog frequent

g = warmest month before solstice (A climate)

GLOSSARY

A-horizon: The topsoil horizon having maximum biological activity, heaviest humus accumulation, and normally the most fertile layer.

Absolute humidity: The actual amount of moisture in the air (expressed as units of weight per volume).

Abyssal (deep): The deepest portion of the ocean.

Adiabatic lapse rate: The increase or decrease of air temperatures due to compression or expansion of air.

Air masses: A body of air, within which the temperature, humidity and pressure are relatively uniform.

Alluvial fans: A deposit of sediments generally associated with mountain streams, marking a sudden reduction in velocity of flow due to a change in gradient from steep to relatively flat.

Alluvium: Sediments deposited on land by streams.

Altimeter: An aneroid barometer which is scaled to record altitude.

Anemometer: An instrument used to measure wind velocity.

Aneroid barometer: A device which records atmospheric pressure through the use of a sealed metallic chamber from which most of the air has been removed.

Anticline: An upward fold in rock.

Antipode: The opposite point on the earth's surface from a given point.

Aphelion: The greatest distance between the earth and sun.

Aquifer: A water-bearing formation through which water moves more readily than in adjacent rock formations.

Arête: A serrate mountain ridge created by mountain glaciers.

Artesian: The rising of ground water above the earth's surface through natural or mechanical pressure.

Atmosphere: The gaseous envelope surrounding the earth.

Atmospheric pressure: The weight of the atmosphere.

Aurora borealis: The Northern Lights.

Azimuth: The angular distance measured in the horizontal plane.

Azonal soil: A soil which has no well-developed soil profile characteristics.

B-horizon: The soil horizon usually immediately below the topsoil. It is sometimes termed "subsoil."

Baguio: The Philippine term for typhoon or hurricane.

Bar: A deposit of sand and similar debris left by waves or currents.

Basalt: A dark, fine-grained igneous rock.

Batholith: A large bulbous igneous intrusion frequently found at the core of mountain ranges.

Biogeography: The study of extant plant and animal communities.

Block diagram: A cartographic device used to show topography in three dimensions.

Block mountain: A mountain which is uplifted along a fault plane.

Boss (stock): An irregularly shaped igneous intrusion.

Brown earth soils: A zonal group of soils having a brown surface. They are moderately well endowed with humus, and quite fertile. They develop under short grasses, bunch-grass, and shrubs at the inner margins of steppe climates.

C-horizon: The unconsolidated rock layer from which the upper soil horizons have developed.

Calcification: The process by which soils become basic and accumulate calcium carbonate within subhumid, semiarid, or arid climates.

Caldera: A large volcanic crater.

Capillary water: The water held by surface tension upon soil particles and occupying a portion of the pore space between them.

Carbonization: The infusion of CO_2 with water to produce a weak solution of acid.

Cartogram: A cartographic device used to show distribution of commodities.

Cartography: The art and science of map making.

Chaparral: Vegetation which is characterized by drouth-resistant, dense, shrubby trees. Also, variously termed maquis, macchia, and mallee.

Chernozem soils: A zonal group of soils having deep, dark surface horizons and rich in organic matter. They develop under tall mixed grasses in a subhumid climate.

Chestnut earth soils: A zonal group of soils with dark-brown surface horizons. They develop under short mixed grasses in a climate where rainfall is light and erratic.

Chinook winds: In North America, warm drying winds descending the leeward slopes of the Rocky Mountains.

Chronometer: A very accurate timepiece.

Cirque: An ampitheater-like basin created by ice-scour in mountainous regions.

Clastic rocks: Sedimentary rocks which are composed of particles cemented together by a fine matrix.

Climate: A composite of weather conditions over a long period of time.

Climatology: The analytical study of the climates of the world.

Climax soil: The end product of soil-forming processes in a particular physical environment.

Climax vegetation: The process of certain species of vegetation becoming dominant through natural selection and adaptation within a specific climatic region.

Col: A small saddle or pass cut through a mountain range by moving ice.

Cold front: The contact zone where cold air displaces warm air.

Condensation: The change in state from a gaseous to a liquid form.

Conduction: The transfer of heat by direct contact between two bodies.

Conglomerate: A sedimentary rock composed of a mixture of more or less rounded stones and gravel cemented together by natural elements.

Conic projection: A type of projection where the earth's grid is projected onto a tangent or secant cone.

Coniferous: A cone-bearing, needle-leaf tree.

Constructive forces: Those physical forces which contribute to the building up of the earth's surface.

Continental plateau: A plateau or tableland which rises abruptly on at least one side from bordering lowlands or from seas and generally having no contiguous mountain rim.

Continental shelf: The submerged extension of the continents whose outer edge drops abruptly to the deep sea floor.

Continental slope: A very steep slope of the continents at the outer edge of the continental shelf.

Contour lines: Lines drawn on a map through points of equal elevation generally referred to sea-level.

Contour map: A map using contour lines to depict surface relief.

Convection: The process of transferring heat energy by the motion of a gas or liquid.

Convectional precipitation: Precipitation caused by rising air which cools below the dew point.

Core: The innermost zone of the earth. It is surrounded by the mantle.

Crust: The outermost zone of the earth. It rests upon the mantle.

Cultural geography: The study of features resulting from man's settlement of the earth.

Cyclone: Any low pressure area or storm which is also termed a low.

Cyclonic precipitation: Precipitation resulting from cold, dense air meeting warmer, lighter air and cooling the warmer air.

D-horizon: A layer of unweathered rock material underlying the soil horizons.

Deciduous: Vegetation which drops its leaves in rhythmic response to the seasons.

Decomposition: The chemical decay of rocks.

Deflation: The process of removal of small particles of material by the action of the wind.

Delta: A built-up deposit of excessive sediments marking the place where a stream enters a pond, lake, or sea whose waters are generally quiet.

Desert: A type of climate which is characterized by extreme temperature variations, low humidity, and limited rainfall usually less than 10 inches.

Desert soils: A zonal group of soils that have light-colored surfaces that developed under xerophytic vegetation in arid climates.

Destructive forces: Those physical forces which are attempting to wear down the earth's surface.

Dew point: The temperature at which air becomes saturated.

Diastrophism: A constructive force characterized by crustal movements.

Dike: An igneous intrusion into a vertical joint or crack.

Disintegration: The mechanical breaking down of rocks into smaller fragments.

Doldrums: An area generally between 5° north latitude and 5° south latitude, in which calm and light ascending air currents prevail.

Drift: Glacial deposited materials left after the ice has receded.

Drumlin: A smooth egg-shaped hill composed of till deposited on the surface of till plains.

Dry adiabatic lapse rate: The rate at which the temperature decreases with the movement of air upward. The rate of temperature decrease is 5.5°F. per 1,000 feet.

Dry subtropical: A type of climate where annual precipitation is generally between 15 and 25 inches, mostly occurring during the winter season. It is normally characterized by hot summers and mild winters.

Dune: A hill or ridge of sand deposited by wind erosion.

Ecliptic: The plane in which the earth revolves around the sun.

Ecological succession: The sequence of low orders of vegetation being replaced by higher types of vegetation.

Economic geography: The study of the production, consumption, and distribution of goods and services.

Eluviation: The movement of material within the soil by suspension in descending moisture.

Emerging coastlines: Shorelines which normally have a smooth, slightly dipping plane into the sea without significant indentations.

Epiphytes: Plants which attach themselves to other plants, but do not secure their food supply from them.

Equinox: The two times during a year that the noon sun is vertical at the equator.

Erosion: The transfer of loose materials from where they are to some other location by streams, ice, wind, waves, or ground water.

Escarpment: The steep face of a sloping rock formation.

Exfoliation: The process of flaking off of small plates of rock from a larger rock mass.

Fall line: The point at which an abrupt change in the gradient of a stream occurs when the latter's bed shifts from a hard stratum to a soft one.

Fault: A break across rock strata resulting in the displacement of the rock formation on at least one side of the fracture.

Fauna: The native animal life characteristic of a geographic region.

Fiord: A deeply gouged glacial valley occupied by an arm of the sea.

Flat plain: An area having a local relief of less than 50 feet and an elevation of less than 2,000 feet.

Flood plain: An area along a stream which is flooded in time of high water.

Flora: Native plants or native plant life which is characteristic of a geographic region.

Foehn winds: A warm wind descending the leeward sides of

mountains in Europe; same as chinook winds in North America.

Fracture: A break in rock.

Front: The zone of contact between two air masses.

Frost wedging: The rupturing of rock and prying the mineral grains apart by the freezing of water.

Galactic rotation: The rotation of any galaxy.

Galaxy: A family of stars.

Geodesy: The science which deals with the shape and form of the earth.

Geologic erosion: The reduction of landforms by agents of erosion, such as running water, wind, and moving ice.

Geomorphology: The study of land forms.

Glacier: A large body of moving ice.

Gnomonic projection: A map projection in which the earth's grid is presumed to be projected onto a tangent plane from a light source placed at the center of the earth.

Graben: A landform which has dropped down between two parallel faults.

Gravitational water: Water which percolates downward through the soil between the individual soil particles or aggregates of soil particles.

Gray-brown podsol: A zonal group of soils having grayish-brown layers which rest upon a brown horizon. They are formed under deciduous forests in a moist climate.

Ground moraine: Glacial debris scattered over the surface upon which ice formerly rested.

Ground water: Water, primarily from precipitation that sinks into the ground and occupies the cracks, pores, and other openings in the earth.

Hachure: Shaded lines drawn up and down slopes which give the impression of a third dimension.

Hardwood (tree): A broad-leaf tree.

High: A mass of air in which the circulation is downward, outward, and clockwise in the northern hemisphere.

Hill: An area having an elevation greater than 500 feet and a local relief of more than 500 feet but less than 2,000 feet.

Homolsine: A compromise projection which incorporates some of the features of both the Mollweide and sinusoidal projections.

Horizon (soil): A layer of soil with distinct physical and chemical characteristics.

Horizontal fault: A fault in which the rock moved laterally along the zone of fracture.

Horn: A sharp, pointed mountain peak created by the erosive action of a number of glaciers.

Horst: A block of rock between two faults which stands above the blocks on either side.

Humid continental: A type of climate which is characterized by maximum rainfall during summer, although it is often fairly well distributed throughout the year. Annual precipitation generally is not less than 20 inches. It has hot summers and cold winters.

Humus: The semi-decayed remains of plant and animal life found in soils.

Hurricane: A large and violent cyclonic storm which develops in the Atlantic Ocean. Winds reach a velocity of at least 75 miles per hour.

Hydration: The chemical combination of water with other compounds.

Hydrologic cycle: See water cycle.

Hydrology: The science which deals with the earth's surface and underground waters.

Hydrosphere: The earth's water which covers about 72 per cent of the globe.

Hygrometer: An instrument which measures relative humidity of the air.

Hygroscopic water: A microscopically thin film around each individual soil particle.

Hypsometric map: A specialized variety of contour map which uses color tints between successive contour lines to show relief.

Ice-scour: The erosive action of moving ice.

Igneous rock: A mixture of minerals that have solidified together from naturally occurring earth materials originally in the molten state.

Insolation: The amount of solar energy received at the earth's surface.

Interlobate moraine: Ice deposited debris between two lobes or tongues of ice.

Intermontane plateau: A plateau surrounded by mountains.

International Date Line: The line which approximates the 180° meridian along which date changes are made.

Intertropical front: The boundary between the trade wind systems of the northern and southern hemispheres.

Intrazonal soil: A soil having developed primarily because of parent material or age control rather than climate and vegetation.

Ionosphere: The layer upward of about 25 to 50 miles, consisting of electrically charged particles called ions.

Isobar: A line which connects points having the same barometric pressure.

Isotherm: A line which connects points having the same temperature.

Jet stream: Strong winds located at the upper levels of the troposphere which move generally eastward through the mid-latitudes.

Joint: A surface of rock rupture along which no movement has occurred.

Jungle: A dense undergrowth or second growth in tropical forest areas.

Kame: A small, steep-sided, conical-shaped hill formed by glacial meltwater near the ice margins.

Karst: Topography characterized by solution sinks, underground streams, caves, and caverns.

Kettle: A small depression formed by the melting of a covered block of ice.

Laccolith: A toadstool-shaped igneous intrusion.

Lapse rate: The rate at which air temperature normally decreases with an increase in altitude.

Lateral moraine: A ridge of glacial debris which marks the position of the sides of a valley glacier.

Latitude: The angular distance north or south of the equator.

Latosolic soils: A zonal group of soils which are the most weathered and leached of all zonal soils. They are formed under tropical rainforests where the rainfall exceeds 75 inches annually.

Latozation: The process by which soils are leached, eluviated, and become reddish within humid tropical and humid subtropical regions.

Leaching: The removal of materials in solution by the passage of water through the soil.

Legend: A list which defines symbols, and explains the colors or patterns employed on a map.

Liana: Any climbing plant that has roots in the ground.

Lichen: A low order plant commonly growing on bare rock surfaces.

Limestone: A sedimentary rock composed largely of calcite. Some limestones are composed of fragments of fossils; others are formed chemically from the precipitation of calcite from solution.

Loess: A deposit of fine-grained, disc-like fragments blown in place by wind.

Longitude: The angular distance east or west of the prime meridian.

Low: A mass of warm light air in which the winds blow inward, upward, and anti-clockwise in the northern hemisphere. Also called a cyclone.

Macro-organisms: Forms of life, such as earthworms, ants, and beetles, which are useful in soil.

Magma: Molten rock within the earth.

Mangrove: A group of tropical shrubs or small trees which grow in brackish water as tangled swamps.

Mantle: The intermediate zone of the earth. It lies below the crust, and rests upon the iron-nickel core at a depth of about 1,800 miles.

Map projection: A systematic arrangement by which points on the earth's surface are transferred to grid lines on a plane.

Marble: A metamorphic rock composed of crystallized limestone or dolomite.

Marine climate: A type of climate characteristic of the coastal margins and oceanic islands. Its most striking feature is equability of temperature.

Maximum thermometer: A thermometer with a constriction near the base which allows a reading of maximum temperatures.

Medial moraine: A ridge of glacial debris formed by the convergence of two lateral moraines.

Medical geography: The study of the environmental units, concentration, and extent of disease.

Mercator projection: A modified cylindrical projection useful in air navigation.

Mercurial barometer: An instrument for measuring the pressure of the atmosphere.

Metallic minerals: A mineral dominantly metal which is normally hard, yet malleable and possesses a luster.

Metamorphic rocks: Rocks formed from other rocks by pressure, heat, solution, and chemical action.

Meteorology: The science of the atmosphere.

Micro-organisms: Forms of life too small to be seen by the naked eye which cause decay of organic material and make soil nutrients available for plants.

Mineral: A naturally occurring inorganic substance possessing certain physical properties and a definite chemical composition.

Minimum thermometer: A thermometer using an index marker to record mimimum temperatures.

Mogote: A residual limestone hill left standing above an erosion surface in the old age stage of the Karst erosion cycle.

Mollweide: A mathematically developed projection useful for showing world distributions.

Monsoon: A wind that reverses its direction with opposite seasons blowing from continents during winter and from oceans during summer.

Moraine: A general term applied to landforms composed of materials deposited by glaciers.

Mountain: An area of above 3,000 feet in elevation, with small summit area, and with most of the surface in slopes having a relief greater than 2,000 feet.

Neap tide: The tide produced upon the earth's waters when the sun and moon are located 90° apart.

Nebula: An enormously large rotating mass of gas within the Milky Way.

Neck: A solidified lava remnant left in the throat of a dormant or extinct volcano.

Normal fault: A fault in which the rock moved downward along the zone of fracture. Also called a gravity fault.

Oasis: An isolated area within a desert with ground water at or near the surface.

Ocean current: The movement of ocean waters in response to winds, variations in densities, and configuration of ocean basins.

Occluded front: A discontinuity surface formed when one front overtakes another. Typically a cold front catching and over-riding a warm front.

Orographic precipitation: Precipitation which results from air being forced upward over land barriers.

Outwash plain: A flat to gently sloping surface which generally occupies outer margins of till plains that are composed of material carried from a glacier by meltwater.

Oxbow lake: An abandoned stream meander of a winding river.

Ozone layer: A layer of oxygen gases in the lower stratosphere that filters out most of the sun's ultraviolet rays.

Parallel: East-west line parallel to the equator used to measure latitude.

Pedalfer: Aluminum- and iron-accumulating soil characteristic of humid environments.

Pedocal: Calcium-accumulating soils characteristic of subhumid, semiarid or arid environments.

Pedology: Soil science.

Peneplain: An area of little local relief left as the last stage of the water erosion cycle.

Perihelion: When the earth is nearest the sun in early January.

Permafrost: Permanently frozen subsoil.

Permeability: The ability of water to flow through a rock.

pH: A numerical designation of the acidity and alkalinity of soils. A pH of 7 represents an approximately neutral soil condition. High pH numbers indicate alkalinity and low pH numbers indicate acidity.

Physiography: The study of landform changes.

Piedmont plateau: A plateau situated between a mountain and a plain or sea.

Plain: An area of less than 500 feet of local relief and mostly low elevations of less than 2,000 feet.

Plateau: A broad upland of usually more than 2,000 feet elevation which rises abruptly on at least one side above the adjacent area.

Playa lake: An ephemeral lake. Typically salt, usually temporary.

Plug: See neck.

Podsolization: The process by which soils are depleted of bases, become more acid and shallow, and have developed leached surface layers within cool, moist climates.

Podsol soils: A zonal group of soils having a gray leached horizon above a dark brown B-horizon. They are formed under forests in a cool, moist climate.

Polar easterlies: Winds blowing from the poles toward the equator; northeasterlies in the Northern Hemisphere and southeasterlies in the Southern Hemisphere.

Polar front: A transition zone separating an air mass of polar origin from one of tropical origin.

Polar ice cap: A type of climate with less than 10 inches of precipitation and no month which has an average temperature above 32°F.

Pole: 90° N. or S. latitude. The point where the earth's axis intersects the surface of the earth.

Porosity: The amount of pore space in rocks and soils.

Prairie soils: A zonal group of soils having dark-colored surface horizons and formed under tall prairie grasses.

Precession: The wobbling of the earth's axis in a very slow circular motion opposite to the direction of the earth's rotation.

Precipitation: The collective term for rain, snow, sleet, hail, etc., which falls because of rapid condensation.

Prevailing westerlies: The wind belts of the mid-latitudes lying between the subtropical high-pressure belts and the subpolar low-pressure belts.

Prime meridian: The 0° meridian which passes through Greenwich, England.

Profile (soil): A vertical section of the soil through all horizons and into the parent material.

Psychrometer: An instrument for measuring atmospheric humidity.

Radiation: Heat in the form of rays given off by the earth and sun.

Rainshadow: The dry slopes on the leeward side of a mountain range.

Recessional moraine: A moraine formed at the ice margin in a retreating position.

Red earth soils: A zonal group of soils which have thin organic horizons over a yellowish-brown leached horizon. They are formed under forests in humid subtropical climates.

Regolith: The loose, weathered bedrock which lies above solid rock.

Relative humidity: The percentage of moisture which a given volume of air contains relative to saturation at a prevailing temperature.

Relief: The difference in elevation between the highest and lowest points.

Reverse fault: A fault in which the rock moved upward along the zone of fracture.

Revolution: The movement of the earth in an elliptical orbit around the sun.

Rhumb line: A short, straight line which follows the general direction of the great circle, but cuts across the grid lines at a constant angle.

Rift valley: A broad valley bounded by faults.

Roche moutonee: An asymmetrically scoured glacial boulder, which normally has a steep end facing away from the ice source.

Rock: A naturally occurring inorganic substance which is composed of a combination of two or more minerals.

Rolling plain: An area having a local relief of 150 to 300 feet and an elevation of less than 2,000 feet.

Rotation: The movement of the earth upon its axis. The period of rotation is approximately 24 hours.

Rough dissected plain: An area having a local relief of 300 to 500 feet and an elevation of less than 2,000 feet.

Sand dune: An accumulation of sand in a ridge or mound caused by wind deposition.

Sandstone: A sedimentary rock formed by the cementation of individual grains of sand.

Saturation: The condition that exists in the atmosphere when the air contains all the moisture it is capable of holding at the prevailing temperature.

Savanna grassland: Tropical grasslands which are mixed with scattered trees that are usually small and scrubby.

Scale: The ratio between map distance and earth distance.

Schist: A metamorphic rock derived from shale, basalt, or granite.

Schlerophyll: A woodland area in which the leaves are small, stiff, thick, and leathery with hard, shiny surfaces.

Sea arch: An offshore arch resulting from the erosive action of waves.

Sedimentary rocks: Rocks formed from fragments or minerals derived from the disintegration of existing rocks or animal remains.

Selva: Broadleaf evergreen forests which consist of a mixture of many tree species. They are located in a tropical rainforest climate.

Shaded map: A map using light and shadow to depict surface relief.

Sill: A nearly horizontal igneous intrusion between two layers of rock.

Sink: A depression caused by the decomposition of limestone rock by solution.

Sinusoidal: A map projection which has its meridians developed from sine curves.

Slate: A metamorphic rock formed from shale.

Softwood (tree): A needle-leaf tree.

Soil: The unconsolidated material at the top of the mantle rock in which plants may grow.

Solstice: The dates when the sun's vertical rays strike the Tropic of Cancer and the Tropic of Capricorn.

Solution: The dissolving of a material in a solvent.

Spring tide: The tide produced by the sun and moon pulling together upon the waters of the earth.

Stable air: A condition in which a particle of air will resist displacement from its level.

Stacks: Rock pinnacles offshore created by wave erosion.

Steppe: A semiarid climate.

Stock: An irregularly shaped igneous intrusion.

Strata: Layers of sedimentary materials.

Stratosphere: The layer between the troposphere and the ionosphere

Stream: A larger ocean current.

Structure (soil): The arrangement of agglomerations of individual soil particles.

Subarctic: A type of climate which generally has from 10 to 20 inches of precipitation annually with long cold winters, and short mild summers.

Submerging coastlines: Shorelines which have an irregular profile with deep bays which were formerly stream valleys.

Subtropical calms: High pressure centers located between the trade winds and the westerlies.

Syncline: A downward fold in rock strata.

Synoptic chart: A chart or map which shows the distribution of weather conditions of an area for a given period of time.

Systematic geography: The study of a particular aspect of geography within an area or over the surface of the earth.

Taiga: The northern coniferous forest.

Talus: A pile of debris collected at the lower slopes of a hill.

Terminal moraine: A ridge of glacial debris which marks the farthest advance of a glacier.

Texture (soil): The relative proportions of the various size groups of soil particles. It refers to the proportion of sand, silt, and clay.

Thrust fault: A fault in which the rock moved both upward and laterally along the zone of fracture.

Thunderstorm: Any storm accompanied by lightning and thunder.

Tides: The regular movement of the oceans, caused by the gravitational pull of the moon and sun upon the earth's waters.

Till plain: A plain which is composed of unstratified and unsorted glacial drift deposited directly by ice.

Tilth: The workability of a soil in respect to its fitness for plant growth.

Topographic map: A map used to depict landforms.

Topography: The general configuration of the earth's surface.

Tornado: A very violent low-pressure storm accompanied by a funnel-shaped cloud and destructive wind.

Trace elements: Elements found in only small amounts; their function in plant nutrition is, as yet, debatable.

Trade winds: Wind belts on both sides of the equator, extending to about 30° north latitude and 30° south latitude, in which the winds blow from easterly quadrants toward the equatorial low.

Transect chart: A profile which also includes information on physical and cultural features.

Trewartha system: A modified form of the Koeppen system for classifying climates.

Tropical rainforest: A type of climate in which both the monthly and annual temperatures average about 80°F. Annual rainfall commonly varies from about 60 inches to more than 100 inches, with no month receiving less than 2.4 inches.

Tropical red soils: A zonal group of soils which are a variety of latosolic soils but not so thoroughly leached. They are formed under tropical rainforests, tropical savanna, and tropical monsoon environments.

Tropical savanna: A type of climate where average temperatures are similar to those of the tropical rainforest. Annual precipitation is generally between 30 and 60 inches with a wet and dry season.

Tropopause: A region of the atmosphere which marks the base of the stratosphere and the top of the troposphere.

Troposphere: The layer of the air next to the earth's surface which extends upward for about 10 miles to the tropopause.

Tundra: A climatic region with little precipitation, usually less than 10 inches, short and uncertain summers, and long, severe winters.

Tundra soils: A zonal group of soils which are usually grayish in color and strongly acid in reaction. They are formed under tundra vegetation and tundra climates.

Typhoon: A tropical storm which occurs in the Pacific Ocean.

Undulating plain: An area having a local relief of 50 to 150 feet and an elevation of less than 2,000 feet.

Unstable air: A condition in which a particle of air will not settle down into the same area from which it has risen.

Van der Grinten: A map projection which is well suited for showing world distributions.

Volcano: A mountain which periodically ejects lava, ash, sulphurous fumes, and steam through a crater or vent.

Vulcanism: The process of building up a landform by the accumulation and distribution of magma.

Warm front: The zone of contact at the leading edge of a warm air mass which is displacing a colder air mass.

Water (hydrologic) cycle: The circulation of the earth's water supply through evaporation, saturation, condensation, precipitation, and drainage.

Watershed: The drainage basin of any stream.

Waterspout: A tornado-like low pressure storm occurring over a body of water.

Water table: The upper limits of the zone of water saturation.

Wave-cut terrace: A step-like bench created by the erosive action of waves.

Waves: The surface motion of the ocean which is caused by the drag of winds upon the water.

Weather: The state of the atmosphere at any given time.

Weathering: The process of disintegration or decomposition of rocks at or near the earth's surface.

West coast marine: A climate characterized by precipitation occurring throughout the year. Maximum precipitation occurs during the winter season, and temperatures are unusually mild for these latitudes throughout the year.

Westerlies: Wind belts located poleward from the subtropical calms. They are southwesterly winds in the Northern Hemisphere and northwesterly winds in the Southern Hemisphere.

Wet subtropical: A climatic region where annual rainfall is 30 to 65 inches, with the maximum rainfall occurring during the summer months. Hot summers and mild winters characterize the temperatures.

Willy-willie: The Australian term for typhoon or hurricane.

Wind: Horizontal, or nearly horizontal movements of air in motion. Vertical air movements are called "air currents."

Wind vane: A simple device used to indicate wind direction.

Xerophyte: Dry land vegetation, which is structurally adapted for growth with a limited water supply.

Zenith angle: The angle between the sun's vertical rays and a line rising vertically from an observer.

Zonal soil: A soil having well-developed characteristics in response to climate and natural vegetation.

FINAL EXAMINATIONS

Matching: From the right-hand column, select the phrase or statement which best defines or explains each of the terms in the left-hand column.

1. longitude

2. meridians

3. Tropic of Cancer

4. parallels

5. equinox

6. rotation

7. latitude

8. orbit

9. ellipse

10. revolution

a. Angular distance on the surface of the earth east or west of prime meridian.

b. The shape of the path followed by the earth around the sun.

c. The parallel at 23½ degrees north latitude.

d. The parallel at 23½ degrees south latitude.

e. Angular distance on the surface of the earth north or south of the equator.

f. The motion of the earth around the sun.

g. The turning of the earth on its axis.

h. The date on which days and nights are equal everywhere on earth.

i. The shortest lines from pole to pole on the surface of the earth.

j. The lines which extend east-west on the surface of the earth.

k. The path of the earth around the sun.

Multiple Choice: Select the letter which represents your choice.

11. The vertical distance between two contour lines is called the: (a) contour; (b) gradient; (c) scale; (d) contour interval.

12. You are asked to secure a map of the world on which directions can be easily and accurately determined. You would probably secure: (a) a conical projection; (b) an orthographic projection; (c) Mercator's projection; (d) another job.

13. The fractional scale 1/63,360 means that one inch on the map equals: (a) 12 miles; (b) 1 mile; (c) 63,360 miles; (d) 63,360 feet on the earth's surface.

14. The constituent of the atmosphere that can best be correlated

with weather is: (a) oxygen; (b) carbon dioxide; (c) nitrogen; (d) water vapor.

15. The pattern of circulation around a low pressure area in the northern hemisphere is: (a) counterclockwise and away from the center; (b) clockwise and away from the center; (c) counterclockwise and toward the center; (d) clockwise and toward the center; (e) none of these.

16. In the northern hemisphere, if a person faces the wind (that is, the wind blows directly toward his face), the center of a low pressure area could be found: (a) at his right; (b) directly behind him; (c) at his left; (d) in front of him; (e) at any of the above positions depending upon where the front is located.

17. The outstanding difference between the Humid Subtropical and the Mediterranean or Dry Subtropical Climates is: (a) temperature; (b) amount and distribution of rainfall; (c) amount of sunlight; (d) none of these.

18. Seasonal distribution of precipitation in the Tropical Rainforest type of climate is best described as: (a) pronounced winter dry season; (b) all months wet; (c) maximum precipitation in the coldest months; (d) all months dry.

19. The middle latitude deserts lie within the: (a) horse latitudes; (b) trade winds; (c) prevailing westerlies; (d) subpolar lows.

20. The Humid Subtropical Climate is characteristic of: (a) east coasts of continents just outside the tropics; (b) west coasts of continents just outside the tropics; (c) east coasts of continents just within the tropics; (d) west coasts of continents just within the tropics.

21. Streams tend to deposit their load of sediment as the velocity of flow is decreased. When such occurs at the mouth of a stream, the stream deposits: (a) a delta; (b) an alluvial fan; (c) a flood plain; (d) a bar.

22. The most widespread of the four main erosional agents is: (a) wind; (b) ice; (c) running water; (d) the ocean.

23. The continents are cut up by lesser relief features. The feature which is characterized by low relief and high elevation is a: (a) plain; (b) plateau; (c) hill; (d) mountain; (e) basin.

24. Indented coasts with good harbors are most common in: (a) submerging coasts; (b) emerging coasts; (c) old streams; (d) plateaus; (e) deserts.

25. The Colorado River as it flows over the Colorado Plateau is: (a) old-age; (b) mature; (c) young; (d) rejuvenated.

26. The rainfall where latosols soils develop is generally: (a) less than 20 inches per annum; (b) between 10 and 20 inches per annum; (c) more than 60 inches per annum; (d) characterized by a 9-month dry season; (e) less than 10 inches per annum.

27. Podsol soils develop under: (a) heavy leaching; (b) accumulations of lime; (c) the presence of loess; (d) coniferous or mixed forest vegetation; (e) the accumulation of ashes from forest fires.

28. Chernozem soils have developed under: (a) grass vegetation; (b) tropical rainforest vegetation; (c) coniferous forest vegetation; (d) tundra vegetation; (e) desert shrub.

29. A mature soil which has well-developed characteristics in response to climate and natural vegetation is termed: (a) transported soil; (b) zonal soil; (c) weathered soil; (d) tundra vegetation; (e) desert shrub.

30. A tundra soil would be found in: (a) New England; (b) the southeastern coastal states; (c) the southern great plains; (d) no part of the United States; (e) some part of the United States but none of the above areas.

31. The most important single factor in soil formation is: (a) surface configuration of the land; (b) drainage; (c) the nature of the bed-rock; (d) the degree of soil erosion; (e) climate.

32. In the Tropical Savanna: (a) the forest is too closely spaced to permit grass growth on the forest floor; (b) the forest is very closely spaced; (c) the forest is sufficiently open to permit the growth of grass; (d) there is no grass.

33. Chaparral vegetation would be found in: (a) Indiana; (b) Iowa; (c) Oregon; (d) Florida; (e) California.

34. The climate in which trees have excessive development of xerophytic characteristics is: (a) subpolar; (b) tropical rainforest; (c) tropical savanna; (d) desert; (e) humid subtropical.

35. Mosses and lichens are most common to: (a) deserts; (b) tundra; (c) tropical savanna; (d) subpolar; (e) steppes.

36. The greatest number and widest variety of plant and animals would be found in: (a) deserts; (b) tundra; (c) tropical savanna; (d) subpolar; (e) tropical rainforests.

37. The water table generally: (a) is found only in regions of heavy rainfall; (b) follows the contour of the land; (c) falls during rainfall because of increased weight; (d) is found in regions covered mostly with the sloping sides of hills; (e) has all of the above as its characteristics.

38. The Mississippi Delta was formed: (a) as the flood plains pushed their way out into the Gulf of Mexico; (b) by stream deposition caused chiefly by an increase in velocity due to an increase in the amount of water near the Gulf; (c) by stream deposition due to longshore currents; (d) by stream deposition due to a decrease in the velocity as the stream waters enter the quiet waters of the Gulf; (e) by deposition caused by an increase in friction as the stream floods its banks.

39. An essential condition for the successful drilling of an artesian well is the existence of a: (a) meandering stream; (b) sloping layer of pervious rock between layers of impervious rock; (c) spring at the lowest level in a valley; (d) pervious rock layer in the form of an anticline.

40. In two alternate rock layers the sandstone rock contains vast quantities of water, but the shale which lies underneath it does not. The best explanation of this situation is: (a) The permeability of shale is greater; (b) the porosity of shale is greater; (c) the permeability of sandstone is greater; (d) the porosity of sandstone is greater.

FINAL EXAMINATION 2

Multiple Choice: Select the proper expression in each statement in the following lists of questions.

1. One of the following is *not* one of the physical elements of geography: (a) weather; (b) fishing; (c) oceans; (d) landforms; (e) climate.

2. The elements of the physical setting include: (a) soils; (b) farming; (c) fishing; (d) mining; (e) settlements.

3. In order to represent the earth with the least amount of distortion, one should use: (a) the globe; (b) a cylindrical projection; (c) a conic projection; (d) a stereographic projection; (e) an orthographic projection.

4. Which one of the following is not a map essential? (a) title; (b) legend; (c) scale; (d) agonic lines; (e) direction.

5. The Milky Way is: (a) a ring of dust or gas around the earth; (b) a galaxy of stars; (c) mist in the air; (d) a beam of sunlight; (e) a group of meteors.

6. The planets are kept in motion in their orbits by: (a) rotation of the sun on its axis; (b) gravitation and centrifugal force; (c) their great size and spherical shape; (d) their distance from the sun; (e) their rotation and density.

7. How long does it take the earth to travel around the sun?

(a) one month; (b) 360 days; (c) 30 days; (d) one week;
(e) 365¼ days.

8. The sun is the center of: (a) all the stars; (b) the solar system;
(c) the sky; (d) the moon's orbit; (e) the Milky Way.

9. The smallest planet is: (a) Mars; (b) Earth; (c) Mercury;
(d) Jupiter; (e) Neptune.

10. The largest member of our solar system is: (a) the Earth;
(b) Neptune; (c) Jupiter; (d) the Sun; (e) the Moon.

11. The name of the largest planet is: (a) Saturn; (b) Jupiter;
(c) Mercury; (d) Mars; (e) Neptune.

12. The solar system includes: (a) the sun and the planets; (b) only
the sun, the earth and the moon; (c) the North Star and the sun;
(d) all heavenly bodies; (e) all the stars.

13. An eclipse of the sun is caused by: (a) the passage of the sun
between the moon and the earth; (b) a huge sun spot; (c) the
shadow of the moon; (d) the shadow of the earth; (e) the passage
of a black cloud over the sun.

14. The process by which heat is transmitted from the sun to the
earth is: (a) conduction; (b) convection; (c) radiation; (d) weathering; (e) cosmic disturbances.

15. Relative humidity: (a) increases with increased temperature;
(b) decreases with increased temperature; (c) decreases with decreased
temperature; (d) is not affected by temperature changes; (e) increases
with increased pressure.

16. The instrument used to record continuous changes of pressure is
a: (a) hygrograph; (b) thermograph; (c) barometer; (d) anemometer; (e) barograph.

17. The lower temperature on a wet-bulb thermometer is caused by:
(a) increased pressure; (b) increased temperature; (c) decreased
pressure; (d) evaporation; (e) decreased temperature.

18. The type of precipitation which results from the heating of surface
air which then rises and cools is: (a) orographic; (b) conductional;
(c) convectional; (d) radiational; (e) cyclonic.

19. A region or station typical of the Mediterranean Climate is:
(a) Los Angeles; (b) Miami; (c) Seattle; (d) Cairo, Egypt.

20. Typical precipitation amounts of the tropical rainforest climate
would be: (a) 20 inches; (b) 30 inches; (c) 40 inches; (d) 60 or
more inches.

21. (a) Basic lavas; (b) acidic lavas weather into better agricultural
soils.

22. In the Tropical Savanna the rainfall is: (a) less in amount and less dependable; (b) more in amount and less dependable; (c) less in amount and more dependable; (d) more in amount and more dependable than the Tropical Rainforest.

23. The Marine West Coast Climate occurs: (a) where the horse latitudes blow from the ocean over the land; (b) where the westerlies blow from the ocean over the land; (c) where the horse latitudes blow from the land over the ocean; (d) where the westerlies blow from the land over the oceans.

24. The native vegetation typical of the Marine West Coast Climate is: (a) coniferous forests; (b) grassland; (c) hardwood forests; (d) savanna.

25. Weathering changes solid bedrock into loose debris which accumulates around the base of the parent rock. This mass of small rock fragments is called: (a) soil; (b) mantle rock; (c) sandstone; (d) igneous rock; (e) subsoil.

26. The mechanical breaking down of rocks into smaller fragments is known as: (a) decomposition; (b) oxidation; (c) carbonation; (d) hydration; (e) disintegration.

27. The rust that covers a piece of steel when exposed to weathering is caused by: (a) disintegration; (b) oxidation; (c) carbonation; (d) hydration; (e) solution.

28. Rocks formed in layers under water are: (a) igneous; (b) firemade; (c) stratified; (d) metamorphic; (e) reheated.

29. A sedimentary rock which is made from stratified mud is: (a) sandstone; (b) shale; (c) conglomerate; (d) granite; (e) basalt.

30. An example of a volcano which erupted with enough explosive power to blow an island to bits was: (a) Vesuvius; (b) Krakatoa; (c) Mauna Loa; (d) Stromboli; (e) Mt. Lassen.

31. About 80 per cent of all volcanoes are concentrated along the: (a) Pacific Ocean; (b) Mediterranean Sea; (c) Atlantic Ocean; (d) Indian Ocean; (e) Gulf of Mexico.

32. Under similar conditions of rock type, structure, surface configuration and rainfall, the water table would be: (a) higher where the surface cover was bare soil; (b) higher where the soil was sandy; (c) higher where the soil was thick, heavy clay; (d) higher where the land was forested; (e) the same in all the above cases.

33. Of the following rock types, which one is likely to yield the most abundant supply of ground water? (a) granite; (b) basalt;

(c) sandstone; (d) limestone; (e) shale.

34. A measure of the ease with which water can move through rocks is known as: (a) porosity; (b) permeability; (c) structure; (d) saturation; (e) water table.

35. If the rocks of a region are stratified, which one of the following do we know about the history of the region: (a) that there have been no earthquakes; (b) that caves were once common; (c) that it was formerly a volcanic region; (d) that it is igneous rock; (e) that the land was once under water.

36. A dark colored coarse grained igneous rock is: (a) granite; (b) basalt; (c) limestone; (d) shale.

37. The metamorphic equivalent of sandstone is: (a) quartzite; (b) marble; (c) schist; (d) granite.

38. A clastic sedimentary rock is: (a) limestone; (b) conglomerate; (c) gneiss; (d) marble.

39. A study of surface changes of the earth is: (a) climatology; (b) meteorology; (c) physiography; (d) geodesy.

40. An area of coarse grass interrupted here and there with trees is: (a) selva; (b) taiga; (c) savanna; (d) schlerophyll.

FINAL EXAMINATION 3

Multiple Choice: Select the letter which represents your choice.

1. Cultural geography is chiefly concerned with: (a) religious history; (b) the Fine Arts and history; (c) man's transformation of earth's surface; (d) population distribution; (e) distribution of earth's economic resources.

2. Mercator projection is a mathematical adaptation from which of the following types of geometric figures: (a) cylinder; (b) circle; (c) square; (d) cone; (e) plane.

3. A gnomonic map projection is projected from: (a) North Pole; (b) equator; (c) the antipode; (d) center of the earth; (e) infinity.

4. On a contour map the steepness of the slope is shown by: (a) brown lines; (b) blue lines; (c) black lines; (d) green lines; (e) brown squares.

5. The most satisfactory map projection for navigation is: (a) seismic; (b) stereographic; (c) Mollweide; (d) Mercator; (e) Van der Grinten.

6. A general description of the surface features of the earth is called:

(a) volcanism; (b) submergence; (c) topography; (d) relief; (e) contours.

7. A dictionary of geographic names is known as: (a) an atlas; (b) a gazetteer; (c) a globe; (d) relief map; (e) secondary source.

8. Lines used to measure latitude are known as: (a) meridians; (b) contours; (c) prime meridians; (d) bench marks; (e) parallels.

9. A map on which any small quadrangle has the same base length and height as on a globe of the same scale is: (a) conformal; (b) equidistant; (c) equal-area; (d) parametric; (e) polyconic.

10. The length of a degree of latitude is approximately: (a) 70 miles; (b) 40 miles; (c) 60 miles; (d) 20 miles; (e) 10 miles.

11. The Van der Grinten projection would be *least* useful for: (a) economic distributions; (b) climatic zones; (c) population distribution; (d) navigation; (e) vegetation distribution.

12. Rhumb lines are associated chiefly with: (a) Bonne's projection; (b) Mercator projection; (c) Aitoff's projection; (d) navigation; (e) vegetation distribution.

13. Two places are 10 degrees of longitude apart. The difference in local time is: (a) one hour; (b) 40 minutes; (c) 30 minutes; (d) 20 minutes; (e) 10 minutes.

14. On a map one inch represents sixteen miles. The scale is approximately: (a) 1/400,000; (b) 1/1,000,000; (c) 1/80,000; (d) 1/350,000; (e) 1/90,000.

15. Air is a (a) compound; (b) element; (c) rare gas; (d) major constituent; (e) mixture.

16. The atmospheric description: ascending air currents, cumulus clouds, heavy and regular rainfall, sultry and oppressive weather, best fits which one of the following? (a) horse latitudes; (b) doldrums; (c) trade winds; (d) westerlies; (e) polar easterlies.

17. The process by which heat is transmitted from the sun to the earth is: (a) conduction; (b) convection; (c) radiation; (d) weathering; (e) cosmic disturbances.

18. Air masses are best developed during the: (a) fall; (b) winter; (c) spring; (d) summer.

19. Warm ocean currents in higher latitudes cause isotherms to bend, (a) toward the equator; (b) toward the poles; (c) do not cause them to bend; (d) disappear.

20. The type of precipitation which results from the heating of surface air which then rises and cools is: (a) orographic; (b) conductional; (c) convectional; (d) radiational; (e) cyclonic.

The ten following topographic features characterize regions of youth, mature, and old age topography. Name the age with which each is most characteristic.

21. Pronounced meandering of streams with ox-bow lakes.
22. Valleys narrow and gorge-like, usually deep.
23. Limited development of flood-plains in the major streams.
24. Waterfalls and rapids numerous.
25. Beginning of stream meandering in the major rivers.
26. No waterfalls; marshes may be present due to a high water table.
27. General absence of flood-plains; valley walls usually rise directly from the water's edge.
28. Many main streams with many tributaries, usually a dendritic drainage pattern.
29. Valleys extremely broad and gently sloping.
30. Marked development of flood-plains over which the rivers flow in meandering courses.

Identify each of the following climates.

31. A definite hot season during part of the year; rains and hot the remainder of the year. Vegetation is tall, thick grasses.
32. Several months below zero temperatures, low rainfall. Frozen soil during winter, marshy during summer. Greatest temperature extremes of any climate.
33. Moist all year but especially rainy, foggy, and cloudy in winter; definite seasonal change but few extremes of temperature. Summer temperatures average in the low 60's, winter temperatures average in the low 40's, small diurnal changes in the temperature.
34. Moderately rainy in winter, parched and dry in summer. Total rainfall about 20 inches per year; characterized by much irrigation farming inasmuch as the rain occurs during the winter season.
35. About 30 degrees F. in January; about 75 degrees F. in July; thunderstorms in summer, cyclonic rainfall in winter. Mixed forests with mostly hardwoods where land is not cleared. Rainfall is fairly evenly distributed throughout the year.

In the following questions, mark a *if produced by wind erosion;* b *if produced by stream erosion;* c *if produced by underground water;* d *if produced by glaciers, and* e *if produced by the ocean.*

36. Long parallel scratches in boulders
37. V-shaped valleys

38. Caves and caverns
39. Deep, steep-sided U-shaped valleys
40. Loess

FINAL EXAMINATION 4

Multiple Choice: Select the letter which represents your choice.

1. The length of a degree of latitude at 30 degrees North is approximately: (a) 30 miles; (b) 45 miles; (c) 69 miles; (d) 20 miles; (e) 60 miles.

2. A sinusoidal projection is best suited for showing: (a) true direction; (b) true distance; (c) world distribution; (d) California; (e) polar areas.

3. The agonic line joins points having: (a) the same rainfall; (b) the same output of iron ore; (c) the same magnetic declination; (d) the same marine depths; (e) the same wind velocity.

4. A map projection which has straight lines which represent great circles is the: (a) polyconic; (b) gnomonic; (c) simple conic; (d) Alber's conic; (e) Lambert's azimuthal.

5. If the "15 minute" United States Topographic map is enlarged photographically three times its original linear dimensions, the new scale will be approximately: (a) 1/180,000; (b) 1/62,500; (c) 1/31,250; (d) 1/20,830; (e) 1/15,625.

6. The outstanding quality of the Mercator map projection is: (a) equal area; (b) true shapes; (c) true directions; (d) great circles are straight lines; (e) no distortion.

7. Areas are most distorted on the Mercator projection in: (a) Africa; (b) equatorial belt; (c) temperate zones; (d) tropical zones; (e) polar regions.

8. On which of the following projections could a navigator plot a great circle course anywhere as a straight line: (a) sinusoidal; (b) Alber's projection; (c) Mercator; (d) gnomonic; (e) Bonne's projection.

9. On United States Topographic maps cultural features are shown by: (a) red; (b) green; (c) black; (d) blue; (e) brown.

10. Parallels and meridians are straight lines and are respectively parallel on which of the following projections: (a) sinusoidal; (b) Van der Grinten; (c) Mercator; (d) simple conic; (e) polyconic.

11. A scale of one inch to five miles is: (a) 1/63,360; (b) 1/62,500;

(c) 1/316,800; (d) 1/200,000; (e) 1/400,500.

12. The gnomonic projection is used most satisfactorily for: (a) world maps; (b) small areas; (c) economic maps; (d) climatic maps; (e) navigation.

13. Isohyets are lines used to indicate: (a) equal barometric pressure; (b) equal temperature; (c) equal depth of water; (d) equal rainfall; (e) equal wind velocity.

14. The scale of a map is 1/250,000. One inch on the map represents approximately: (a) 2 miles; (b) 5 miles; (c) 4 miles; (d) 10 miles.

15. Why is the relative humidity of air in dwelling houses usually too low during winter? (a) The air loses its small amount of moisture as it circulates through the furnace; (b) stoves absorb moisture out of the air; (c) cold air contains little moisture and heat increases the vapor-holding capacity of the air; (d) the windows are closed during the winter.

16. A sudden fall in the barometer reading would usually indicate: (a) the passing of a storm center; (b) the approach of an anticyclone; (c) a period of settled fair weather; (d) a rapidly falling temperature; (e) the approach of clear, cold weather.

17. In the United States, the air masses and cyclones move generally: (a) eastward; (b) westward; (c) northward; (d) southward; (e) in no particular direction.

18. Bodies of water help to moderate the climate because: (a) heat is given off when water evaporates; (b) the approach of a cyclonic disturbance is relatively important; (c) the specific heat of water is relatively large; (d) water is a good conductor of heat; (e) the warmest water is always found at the surface.

19. A fog differs from a cloud largely in that a fog is: (a) much denser; (b) closer to the ground; (c) of different origin; (d) caused by man's activities; (e) not present on a sunny day.

20. When the relative humidity is 60 per cent and the air temperature is 75 degrees F., a cooling of a given air mass: (a) raises the absolute humidity; (b) lowers the absolute humidity; (c) produces no change in relative humidity; (d) increases the relative humidity; (e) decreases the relative humidity.

Match the following.

21. Desert soils

a. Light-colored leached soils of cool, humid forested region.

22. Podsol soils

b. Light reddish-brown soils of warm temperate to hot, arid regions, under shrub vegetation.

23. Brown earths

c. Dark brown soils of cool and temperate, subhumid to semiarid grasslands.

24. Prairie soils

d. Dark reddish-brown soils of warm temperate, relatively human grasslands.

25. Chestnut earths

e. Red or yellow leached soils of warm temperate, humid forested regions.

26. Sierozem soils

f. Brown soils of cool and temperate semiarid grasslands.

27. Latosols

g. Dark brown to nearly black soils of cool and temperate subhumid grasslands.

28. Chernozem soils

h. Reddish-brown soils of warm temperate to hot, semiarid to arid regions, under mixed shrub and grass vegetation.

29. Red and yellow podsolic soils

i. Very dark brown soils of cool and temperate, relatively humid grasslands.

30. Gray brown podsols

j. Grayish-brown leached soils of temperate humid forested regions.

k. Gray soils of cool to temperate arid regions, under shrub and grass vegetation.

l. Heavily leached iron and aluminum rich soils of the humid tropics.

Match the following terms with their definitions.

31. weathering

a. the break up of rock materials by physical processes.

32. decomposition

b. the general destructive effect of the atmosphere on the lithosphere.

33. solution

c. the process by which oxygen unites with some other substance.

34. oxidation

d. the portion of the earth's surface which has been dissolved by other substances.

35. disintegration

e. the process of separating a compound into its original elements by natural decay.

Match the following series:

36. karst
37. till
38. oxidation
39. stalactite
40. plant roots

a. chemical weathering
b. mechanical weathering
c. deposition by glaciation
d. erosion by ground water
e. deposition by ground water

FINAL EXAMINATION 5

Matching: From the left-hand column, select the phrase or statement which best defines or explains each of the terms in the right-hand column.

1. Soils which develop a zone of lime accumulation on semiarid and arid lands.

1. Park savanna

2. Soil most characteristic of the corn belt of the United States is

2. Selva

3. Mixed trees and grass in a wet dry tropical environment.

3. Pedocals

4. The greatest variety of tree species is encountered in

4. Tundra

5. Shrubform vegetation of the dry subtropical environment.

5. Prairie

6. Mosses and lichens are characteristic of this climatic environment.

6. Maquis

7. Forest vegetation that covers much of Canada.

7. Taiga

8. A type of climate where average temperatures are similar to those of

8. Steppe

tropical rainforest. Annual precipitation is generally between 30 and 60 inches with a wet and dry season.

9. A type of climate in which both the monthly and annual temperatures average about 80°F. Annual rainfall commonly varies from about 60 inches to more than 100 inches, with no month receiving less than 2.4 inches.

9. Marine climate

10. A type of climate characteristic of the coastal margins and oceanic islands. Its most striking feature is equability of temperature.

10. West coast marine

11. A type of climate which is characterized by maximum rainfall during summer, although it is often fairly well distributed throughout the year. It has hot summers and cold winters.

11. Tropical rainforest

12. A type of climate which is characterized by extreme temperature variations, low humidity, and limited rainfall.

12. Desert

13. A semi-arid climate.

13. Humid continental

14. A type of climate where annual precipitation is generally between 15 and 25 inches, occurring mostly during the winter season. It is characterized by hot summers and mild winters.

14. Dry subtropical

15. A climate characterized by precipitation occurring throughout the year. Maximum precipitation occurs during the winter season, and temperatures are unusually mild for these latitudes throughout the year.

15. Tropical savanna

16. A climatic region where annual rainfall is 30 to 65 inches, with the maximum rainfall occurring during the summer months. Hot summers and mild winters characterize the temperatures.

16. Wet subtropical

17. A line which connects points having the same barometric pressure.

18. A line which connects points having the same temperature.

19. The line which approximates the 180° meridian although in some places it deviates from that longitude.

20. The 0° meridian which passes through Greenwich, England.

21. Shaded lines drawn up and down slopes which give the impression of a third dimension.

22. A short, straight line which follows the general direction of the great circle, but cuts across the grid lines at the same angle.

23. The angular distance east or west of the prime meridian.

24. The angular distance north or south of the equator.

25. An area of less than 500 feet of local relief and mostly low elevations of less than 2,000 feet.

26. An area having a local relief of 50 to 150 feet and an elevation of less than 2,000 feet.

27. A plain which is composed of unstratified and unsorted glacial drift deposited directly by ice.

28. An area having a local relief of 300 to 500 feet and an elevation of less than 2,000 feet.

29. An area having a local relief of 150 to 300 feet and an elevation of less than 2,000 feet.

30. A flat to gently sloping surface which generally occupies outer margins of till plains that are composed of material carried from a glacier by meltwater.

17. Rhumb line

18. Prime meridian

19. Longitude

20. Isobar

21. Latitude

22. Isotherm

23. International Date Line

24. Hachure

25. Rolling plain

26. Rough dissected plain

27. Plain

28. Outwash plain

29. Undulating plain

30. Till plain

31. The science of the atmosphere.
32. The study of landforms.
33. The analytical study of the climates of the world.
34. The art and science of map making.
35. The temperature of air when saturated with moisture.
36. Precipitation which results from air being forced upward over land barriers.
37. Precipitation resulting from cold, dense air meeting warmer, lighter air and cooling the warmer air.
38. Precipitation caused by rising air which cools rapidly below the dew point.
39. Any low pressure area or storm which is also termed a low.
40. The deepest portion of the ocean.
41. The water which is held by surface tension upon soil particles and occupies a portion of the pore space between them.
42. A deeply gouged glacial valley occupied by the sea.
43. A microscopically thin moisture film around each individual soil particle.
44. The earth's water which covers about 72 per cent of the globe.
45. An inland salt lake.
46. The collective term for rain, snow, sleet, hail, etc., which fall because of rapid condensation.
47. The drainage basin of any stream.
48. A tornado-like low pressure storm occurring over a body of water.
49. The upper limits of the zone of water saturation.

31. Climatology
32. Meteorology
33. Cartography
34. Geomorphology
35. Convectional precipitation
36. Cyclone
37. Dew point
38. Cyclonic precipitation
39. Orographic precipitation
40. Playa lake
41. Precipitation
42. Watershed
43. Water cycle
44. Abyssal
45. Water table
46. Fiord
47. Hydrosphere
48. Waterspout
49. Hygroscopic water

50. The circulation of the earth's water supply through evaporation, saturation, condensation, precipitation, and drainage.

50. Capillary water

FINAL EXAMINATION 6

Multiple choice: Select the letter of the one best answer.

1. The wet season in the tropical monsoon is: (a) in summer; (b) in winter; (c) year around.

2. Wet and dry seasons in the Mediterranean are caused by shifts of prevailing westerlies and (a) doldrums; (b) northeast trades; (c) subtropical highs; (d) polar easterlies.

3. A long sinuous ridge, composed of roughly stratified material describes: (a) drumlin; (b) esker; (c) kame; (d) outwash plain.

4. Unassorted debris deposited beneath glacial ice is: (a) terminal moraine; (b) recessional moraine; (c) interlobate moraine; (d) ground moraine.

5. Hills of glacial debris, shaped like an egg cut in two lengthwise, are: (a) eskers; (b) kames; (c) drumlins; (d) roche moutonnée.

6. Toadstool-shaped igneous intrusions are: (a) dikes; (b) sills; (c) batholiths; (d) laccoliths.

7. A recently formed (1943) Mexican volcano is: (a) Vesuvius; (b) Krakatoa; (c) Pelee; (d) Paracutin.

8. Solution is especially apparent in areas of: (a) sandstone; (b) granite; (c) limestone; (d) shale.

9. An upfold in rock is: (a) graben; (b) horse; (c) anticline; (d) syncline.

10. A surface which has been reduced to base level by degradational forces is: (a) interfluve; (b) peneplain; (c) natural levee; (d) schist.

11. An amphitheater-like ice-scour feature is: (a) horn; (b) col; (c) cirque; (d) arête.

12. Fine wind-blown material is known as: (a) sand; (b) alluvium; (c) gravel; (d) loess.

13. An up-thrust block between two faults is known as: (a) horst; (b) graben; (c) kame; (d) scarp.

14. U-shaped valleys are created by the erosive action of: (a) streams; (b) glaciers; (c) waves; (d) wind.

15. A characteristic species of the schlerophyll forest is: (a) maquis; (b) cork oak; (c) greenheart; (d) none of these.

16. The upper level of subsurface saturation is: (a) spring; (b) water table; (c) artesian structure; (d) aquifer.

17. Strata bounding water-bearing stratum in artesian structure should be: (a) porous; (b) impervious; (c) sandstone; (d) both choice a and c.

18. Ecological succession results ultimately in: (a) climax vegetation; (b) natural selection; (c) biotic resource; (d) none of these.

19. Shrubform vegetation in the Mediterranean environment is called: (a) taiga; (b) maquis; (c) selva; (d) tundra.

20. A tabular upland with a local relief in excess of 500 feet would characterize: (a) plain; (b) plateau; (c) hill; (d) mountain.

21. Temperature at which saturation occurs is known as the: (a) potential temperature; (b) vapor pressure; (c) dew point; (d) average lapse rate.

22. The general path of high and low pressure areas across the United States is: (a) westward; (b) eastward; (c) northward; (d) southward.

23. When it is midnight, standard time, in London (0 degrees longitude) it is: (a) 5 a.m.; (b) 5 p.m.; (c) 6 p.m.; (d) 7 a.m.; (e) 7 p.m. in Chicago (90 degrees W.).

24. At point A, whose longitude is 105 degrees west, it is exactly noon. At the same instant, at point Z it is 4 p.m. solar time. The longitude of point Z is: (a) 15 degrees E.; (b) 30 degrees W.; (c) 45 degrees W.; (d) 60 degrees W.

25. The type of precipitation generally associated with the ascent of air over topographic barriers such as mountains or hills is called: (a) convectional; (b) cyclonic; (c) orographic; (d) none of these.

26. Scale is the ratio between map distance and (a) map projection; (b) elevation; (c) earth distance; (d) distance.

27. A man walks 10 miles south, then 10 miles east, and then 10 miles north. At the end of this time he is back at this original spot, which is: (a) South Pole; (b) equator; (c) Tropic of Capricorn; (d) North Pole.

28. The Sierra Nevada Mountains are examples of: (a) folded; (b) faulted; (c) volcanic mountains.

29. Latitude measures distances: (a) east and west of the prime meridian; (b) north and south of the Tropic of Cancer; (c) north and south of the equator; (d) north and south of prime meridian.

30. Weathering is: (a) rock disintegration; (b) erosion; (c) aggradation; (d) eluviation.

31. A chinook is the same as: (a) hamada; (b) the doldrum; (c) foehn.

32. The diurnal equivalent of monsoon wind circulation is: (a) horst and graben; (b) ocean currents; (c) land and sea breezes; (d) none of these.

33. Which of the following is not a lava plateau? (a) Columbia Plateau; (b) northwestern Deccan Plateau; (c) Paraná Plateau of southern Brazil; (d) Plateau of western Australia.

34. Aggregations of soil particles refer to soil: (a) texture; (b) color; (c) structure; (d) tilth.

35. On June 21st an observer catches the sun at an elevation of 50 degrees in his southern horizon. What is the observer's latitudinal position? (a) 23½ degrees N.; (b) 63½ degrees N.; (c) 63½ degrees S.; (d) 40 degrees N.

36. Dry-tolerant plants are: (a) epiphytes; (b) xerophytes; (c) hydrophytes; (d) halophytes.

37. Loess is: (a) azonal; (b) zonal; (c) intrazonal; (d) none of these.

38. Air plants are: (a) xerophytes; (b) epiphytes; (c) parasites; (d) hygrophytes.

39. On a map with a scale of 1/125,000 two points are 2 inches apart. How far apart, in inches, are these same two points on a map with a scale of 1/250,000? (a) 4 inches; (b) 8 inches; (c) ½ inch; (d) 16 inches; (e) 1 inch.

40. Small discontinuous lines used to indicate relief are: (a) isogonic lines; (b) hachures; (c) contours; (d) transects.

41. Neap tides occur during: (a) new and full moons; (b) first and third quarters; (c) at any phase of the moon.

42. The subtropical high pressure belt is normally: (a) a wet region; (b) a dry region; (c) alternating wet and dry.

43. An anticyclone is usually conducive to: (a) foul weather; (b) fair weather; (c) storminess.

44. The lowest zone of the atmosphere is called the: (a) stratosphere; (b) chemosphere; (c) troposphere; (d) tropopause.

45. The following quotation, "Moisture is evaporated from the oceans, carried inland, and precipitated. It is carried back to the oceans by evaporation, by running off the land as surface, and by movement as ground water," describes the: (a) hydrologic cycle; (b) hygroscopic nuclei; (c) dew point; (d) specific humidity.

The receipt of radiant heat at the earth's surface is known as: ͻnduction; (b) insolation; (c) radiation; (d) convection.

. If the highest point in a restricted area is 500 feet and the lowest , 100 feet, 400 feet represents: (a) elevation; (b) relief; (c) height; (d) distance.

48. A line crossing all meridians at a constant angle is: (a) great circle; (b) small circle; (c) rhumb line; (d) none of these.

49. The Deccan Plateau is: (a) lava; (b) disordered crystalline; (c) sedimentary; (d) none of these.

50. Lichens are best associated with: (a) tundra; (b) taiga; (c) selva; (d) epiphyte.

ANSWER KEY

EXAMINATION 1

1. a	9. b	17. b	25. c	33. e
2. i	10. f	18. b	26. c	34. d
3. c	11. d	19. c	27. d	35. b
4. j	12. c	20. a	28. a	36. e
5. h	13. b	21. a	29. b	37. b
6. g	14. d	22. c	30. e*	38. d
7. e	15. c	23. b	31. e	39. b
8. k	16. a	24. a	32. c	40. d

* No part of the contiguous 48 states but present in Alaska.

EXAMINATION 2

1. b	9. c	17. d	25. b	33. c
2. a	10. d	18. c	26. e	34. b
3. a	11. b	19. a	27. b	35. e
4. d	12. a	20. d	28. c	36. b
5. b	13. c	21. a	29. b	37. a
6. b	14. c	22. a	30. b	38. b
7. e	15. b	23. b	31. a	39. c
8. b	16. e	24. a	32. d	40. c

EXAMINATION 3

1. c	10. a	19. b	28. mature	36. d
2. a	11. d	20. c	29. old age	37. b
3. d	12. b	21. old age	30. old age	38. c
4. a	13. b	22. youth	31. tropical	39. d
5. d	14. b	23. mature	savanna	40. a
6. c	15. e	24. youth	32. subarctic	
7. b	16. b	25. mature	33. west costal marine	
8. e	17. c	26. old age	34. dry subtropical	
9. c	18. b	27. youth	35. humid continental	

EXAMINATION 4

1. c	5. d	9. c	13. d	17. a
2. c	6. c	10. c	14. c	18. c
3. c	7. e	11. c	15. c	19. b
4. b	8. d	12. e	16. a	20. d

21.	b	25.	c	29.	e	33.	d	37.	c
22.	a	26.	k	30.	j	34.	c	38.	a
23.	f	27.	l	31.	b	35.	a	39.	e
24.	i	28.	g	32.	e	36.	d	40.	b

EXAMINATION 5

1.	3	11.	13	21.	24	31.	32	41.	50
2.	5	12.	12	22.	17	32.	34	42.	46
3.	1	13.	8	23.	19	33.	31	43.	49
4.	2	14.	14	24.	21	34.	33	44.	47
5.	6	15.	10	25.	27	35.	37	45.	40
6.	4	16.	16	26.	29	36.	39	46.	41
7.	7	17.	20	27.	30	37.	38	47.	42
8.	15	18.	22	28.	26	38.	35	48.	48
9.	11	19.	23	29.	25	39.	36	49.	45
10.	9	20.	18	30.	28	40.	44	50.	43

EXAMINATION 6

1.	a	11.	c	21.	c	31.	c	41.	b
2.	c	12.	d	22.	b	32.	c	42.	b
3.	b	13.	a	23.	c	33.	d	43.	b
4.	d	14.	b	24.	c	34.	c	44.	c
5.	c	15.	b	25.	c	35.	b	45.	a
6.	d	16.	b	26.	c	36.	b	46.	b
7.	d	17.	b	27.	d	37.	a	47.	b
8.	c	18.	a	28.	b	38.	b	48.	c
9.	c	19.	b	29.	c	39.	e	49.	a
10.	b	20.	b	30.	a	40.	b	50.	a

Principal Countries and Regions
of the World*

POLITICAL DIVISION OR REGION		AREA IN SQ. MILES	POPULATION 1960 EST.	POPULATION PER SQ. MI.
Aden (Colony)	(Br.)	80	147,000	1,837
Aden Protectorate	(Br.)	111,971	671,000	6
Afghanistan		250,900	13,310,000	53
Africa		11,635,000	233,718,700	20
Alabama	(U.S.)	51,609	3,228,000	63
Alaska	(U.S.)	586,400	221,000	0.4
Albania		11,097	1,562,000	141
Alberta	(Can.)	255,285	1,172,000	4.6
Algeria	(Fr.)	919,352	10,648,000	11
American Samoa	(U.S.)	76	23,000	302
Andorra		175	6,500	37
Angola	(Port.)	481,226	4,496,000	9.3
Antarctica		5,100,000	. . .	. .
Argentina		1,072,467	20,737,000	19
Arizona	(U.S.)	113,909	1,250,000	11
Arkansas	(U.S.)	53,104	1,756,000	33
Asia		17,035,000	1,691,327,800	99
Australia	(Br. Comm.)	2,974,581	10,050,000	3
Austria		32,365	7,082,000	219
Azores Is.	(Port.)	890	342,000	384
Bahamas	(Br.)	4,404	136,000	30
Bahrain	(Br. Prot.)	231	129,000	558
Basutoland	(Br.)	11,716	742,000	63
Bechuanaland	(Br.)	274,928	368,000	1.3
Belgian Congo	(Bel.)	926,239	13,732,000	15
Belgium		11,775	9,117,000	774
Belgium & Possessions		937,686	27,790,000	30
Bermuda	(Br.)	22	46,000	2,091
Bhutan	(Ind. Prot.)	19,300	670,000	35
Bolivia		424,052	3,366,000	8
Bonin Is.	(U.S. Milit. Govt.)	40	320	8
Brazil		3,286,344	64,837,000	19
British Columbia	(Can.)	366,255	1,452,000	4
Br. Comm. of Nations		12,056,227	608,510,400	50
British Guiana	(Br.)	82,978	558,000	6.7

* Espenshade, E. B., Jr. (editor) *Goode's World Atlas* (Chicago: Rand McNally and Co., 11th Edition, 1960).

POLITICAL DIVISION OR REGION		AREA IN SQ. MILES	POPULATION 1960 EST.	POPULATION PER SQ. MI.
British Honduras	(Br.)	8,864	91,000	10
British Somaliland	(Br.)	67,982	680,000	10
Brunei	(Br.)	2,226	81,000	36
Bulgaria		43,036	7,859,000	182
Burma		261,689	20,303,000	77
California	(U.S.)	158,693	15,335,000	97
Cambodia		7,550	5,056,000	75
Cameroons		166,752	3,303,000	20
Carmeroons, Br.	(Br.)	34,080	1,613,000	47
Canada	(Br. Comm.)	3,851,113	17,118,000	4.5
Canal Zone	(U.S.)	553	60,000	108
Canary Is.	(Sp.)	2,808	879,000	313
Cape Verde Is.	(Port.)	1,557	193,000	124
Central African Rep.	(Fr. Com.)	227,118	1,224,000	5.4
Central America		208,269	10,929,000	52
Ceylon	(Br. Comm.)	25,332	9,643,000	380
Chad. Rep. of	(Fr. Com.)	466,640	2,612,000	5.6
Channel Is.	(Br.)	75.2	101,000	1,343
Chile		286,322	7,560,000	26
China (excl. Formosa)		3,767,751	699,966,000	186
Colombia		439,405	14,105,000	32
Colorado	(U.S.)	104,247	1,785,000	17
Congo Rep. of	(Fr. Com.)	125,890	816,000	6.4
Connecticut	(U.S.)	5,009	2,392,000	478
Cook Is.	(N.Z.)	99	18,000	182
Costa Rica		19,647	1,194,000	61
Cuba		44,217	6,627,000	150
Cyprus		3,572	559,000	156
Czechoslovakia		49,353	13,639,000	276
Dahomey, Rep. of	(Fr. Com.)	44,713	1,750,000	39
Delaware	(U.S.)	2,057	484,000	235
Denmark		16,614	4,580,000	256
Denmark & Possessions		857,116	4,635,000	5
Dist. of Columbia	(U.S.)	69	825,000	11,956
Dominican Republic		18,811	2,929,000	156
Ecuador		104,479	4,191,000	40
Egypt	(U.A.R.)	386,100	25,313,000	65
England & Wales	(Br.)	58,344	52,267,000	896
Ethiopia (incl. Eritrea)		457,147	21,351,000	46
Europe		3,850,000	573,352,600	149
Faeroe Is.	(Den.)	540	36,000	66

POLITICAL DIVISION OR REGION		AREA IN SQ. MILES	POPULATION 1960 EST.	POPULATION PER SQ. MI.
Falkland Is.	(Br.)	4,618	2,000	0.4
Fiji	(Br.)	7,040	385,000	54
Finland		130,085	4,435,000	34
Florida	(U.S.)	58,560	4,781,000	82
Formosa (Taiwan)		13,885	10,323,000	743
France		212,766	44,927,000	211
France & Possessions (Incl. Fr. Com.)		4,211,438	74,172,800	17
French Equatorial Africa (Fr. Com.)		917,931	5,015,400	5.4
French Guiana	(Fr.)	35,126	31,000	0.8
French Oceania	(Fr.)	1,544	144,000	93
French Somaliland	(Fr.)	8,492	69,300	8
French West Africa (Fr. Com.)		1,694,915	17,696,000	10
Gabon, Rep. of	(Fr. Com.)	98,283	434,000	4.4
Gambia	(Br.)	3,978	307,000	77
Georgia	(U.S.)	58,876	3,906,000	66
Germany (Entire)		137,519	72,149,000	524
Germany, East		41,634	16,403,000	394
Germany, West		95,885	55,746,000	581
Ghana	(Br. Comm.)	91,819	4,847,000	53
Gibraltar	(Br.)	2.3	26,000	11,304
Gilbert & Ellice Is.	(Br.)	369	41,000	111
Great Britain & N. Ireland		94,194	52,402,000	556
Great Britain & Poss.		2,499,816	135,303,350	54
Greece		51,169	8,319,000	163
Greenland	(Den.)	840,000	28,900	0.03
Guadeloupe & Deps.	(Fr.)	687	268,000	390
Guam	(U.S.)	206	42,000	204
Guatemala		42,031	2,584,000	61
Guinea, Rep. of		94,945	2,667,000	28
Haiti		10,711	3,492,000	326
Hawaii	(U.S.)	6,423	665,000	103
Honduras		43,266	1,915,000	44
Hong Kong	(Br.)	391	2,877,000	7,358
Hungary		35,909	9,943,000	277
Iceland		39,750	171,000	4
Idaho	(U.S.)	83,557	672,000	8
Ifni	(Sp.)	579	65,000	11
Illinois	(U.S.)	56,400	10,129,000	180

POLITICAL DIVISION OR REGION		AREA IN SQ. MILES	POPULATION 1960 EST.	POPULATION PER SQ. MI.
India (incl Kashmir)	(Br. Comm.)	1,269,506	404,333,000	31
Indiana	(U.S.)	36,291	4,696,000	129
Indonesia		575,893	87,802,000	152
Iowa	(U.S.)	56,290	2,850,000	50
Iran		629,180	20,577,000	32
Iraq		171,554	6,784,000	39
Ireland		27,137	2,893,000	107
Isle of Man	(Br.)	227	57,300	252
Israel		7,990	2,111,000	264
Italy		116,273	49,363,000	424
Ivory Coast, Rep. of	(Fr. Com.)	124,550	3,145,000	25
Japan		142,773	93,031,000	651
Jordan		37,291	1,702,000	45
Kansas	(U.S.)	82,276	2,163,000	26
Kashmir, Jammu &	(Ind.)	82,258	4,783,000	58
Kentucky	(U.S.)	40,395	3,072,000	76
Kenya	(Br.)	224,960	6,444,000	28
Korea, North		47,811	8,083,000	169
Korea, South		37,414	22,834,000	610
Kuwait	(Br. Prot.)	5,998	219,000	36
Laos		91,482	1,754,000	19
Lebanon		4,014	1,719,000	428
Leeward Is.	(Br.)	423	175,300	414
Liberia		42,989	1,350,000	31
Libya		679,358	1,200,000	1.7
Liechtenstein		60.6	16,000	264
Louisiana	(U.S.)	48,523	3,176,000	65
Luxembourg		998	320,000	320
Macao	(Port.)	6.2	228,000	36,774
Maderia Is.	(Port.)	308	289,000	938
Maine	(U.S.)	33,215	959,000	29
Malagash (Madagascar)	(Fr. Com.)	228,510	5,225,000	23
Malaya	(Br. Comm.)	50,677	6,809,000	134
Maldive Is.	(Br. Prot.)	115	83,500	726
Malta (Incl. Gozo)	(Br.)	122	325,000	2,663
Manitoba	(Can.)	251,030	1,010,000	4
Martinique	(Fr.)	425	275,000	647
Maryland	(U.S.)	10,577	3,066,000	290
Massachusetts	(U.S.)	8,257	4,947,000	599

POLITICAL DIVISION OR REGION		AREA IN SQ. MILES	POPULATION 1960 EST.	POPULATION PER SQ. MI.
Mauritania, Islamic Rep. of	(Fr. Com.)	419,390	685,000	1.6
Mauritius & Deps.	(Br.)	809	650,000	803
Mexico		758,061	33,954,000	44
Michigan	(U.S.)	58,216	8,058,000	138
Midway Is.	(U.S.)	2	600	300
Minnesota	(U.S.)	84,068	3,460,000	41
Mississippi	(U.S.)	47,716	2,188,000	46
Missouri	(U.S.)	69,674	4,328,000	62
Monaco		0.6	22,500	37,500
Mongolia		590,966	1,056,000	1.7
Montana	(U.S.)	147,138	693,000	5
Morocco		170,382	10,165,000	60
Mozambique	(Port)	297,654	6,253,000	21
Muscat & Oman		81,979	85,000	1
Nauru	(Austl.)	8	4,300	537
Nebraska	(U.S.)	77,227	1,488,000	19
Nepal		54,330	8,978,000	165
Netherlands		12,526	11,389,000	909
Netherlands & Poss.		227,910	12,345,000	54
Neth. Antilles	(Neth.)	371	202,000	544
Neth. New Guinea	(Neth.)	159,375	754,000	5
Nevada	(U.S.)	110,540	281,000	2
New Brunswick	(Can.)	27,985	615,000	22
New Caledonia	(Fr.)	7,202	81,000	11
Newfoundland	(Can.)	156,155	456,000	2.9
New Guinea Ter.	(Austl.)	93,000	1,409,000	15
New Hampshire	(U.S.)	9,304	595,000	64
New Hebrides	(Fr.-Br.)	5,700	60,000	10
New Jersey	(U.S.)	7,836	5,941,000	758
New Mexico	(U.S.)	121,666	880,000	7
New York	(U.S.)	49,576	16,612,000	335
New Zealand	(Br. Comm.)	103,736	2,332,000	22
Nicaragua		57,128	1,489,000	26
Niger, Rep. of	(Fr. Com.)	459,180	2,515,000	5
Nigeria	(Br.)	350,291	33,441,000	95
Nieu	(N.Z.)	100	5,300	53
Norfolk I.	(Austl.)	13	1,150	88
North America		9,435,000	251,054,000	26
North Borneo	(Br.)	29,386	426,000	14
North Carolina	(U.S.)	52,712	4,632,000	88
North Dakota	(U.S.)	70,665	647,000	9

POLITICAL DIVISION OR REGION		AREA IN SQ. MILES	POPULATION 1960 EST.	POPULATION PER SQ. MI.
Northern Ireland	(Br.)	5,439	1,425,000	262
N. Rhodesia	(Rh. & Nya.)	288,129	2,377,000	8.2
Northwest Ters.	(Can.)	1,304,903	22,000	0.017
Norway		125,032	3,574,000	28
Nova Scotia	(Can.)	21,068	736,000	35
Nyasaland	(Rh. & Nya.)	49,177	2,788,000	56
Oceania		3,310,000	16,054,000	5
Ohio	(U.S.)	42,222	9,553,000	232
Oklahoma	(U.S.)	69,919	2,304,000	33
Ontario	(Can.)	412,582	5,639,000	14
Oregon	(U.S.)	96,981	1,763,000	18
Pacific Is. Tr. Ter.	(U.S.)	685	77,000	112
Pakistan	(Br. Comm.)	364,702	86,733,000	238
Panama		28,745	1,040,000	36
Papua	(Austl.)	90,540	516,000	5.7
Paraguay		157,006	1,736,000	11
Pennsylvania	(U.S.)	45,333	11,238,000	248
Peru		482,133	10,640,000	22
Philippines		115,600	23,721,000	205
Pitcairn (excl. Deps.)	(Br.)	2	150	75
Poland		120,327	29,550,000	245
Portugal		35,589	9,108,000	256
Portugal & Possessions		839,248	22,799,000	27
Portuguese Guinea	(Port.)	13,944	563,000	40
Portuguese India	(Port.)	1,618	647,000	400
Portuguese Timor	(Port.)	7,332	491,000	67
Prince Edward I.	(Can.)	2,184	121,000	55
Puerto Rico	(U.S.)	3,435	2,403,000	700
Qotar	(Br. Prot.)	8,497	41,800	4.9
Quebec	(Can.)	594,860	4,996,000	8
Reunion	(Fr.)	970	334,000	344
Rhode Island	(U.S.)	1,214	883,000	727
Rhodesia & Nyasaland	(Br.)	487,639	7,805,000	16
Romania		91,675	18,398,000	200
Ruanda-Urandi	(Bel.)	20,916	4,941,000	236
St. Helena & Deps.	(Br.)	119	5,900	50
St. Pierre-Miquelon	(Fr.)	93	5,100	55
Salvador, El		8,260	2,556,000	309
San Marino		23.5	15,100	642
Sao Tome & Principe	(Port.)	372	65,000	175
Sarawak	(Br.)	47,069	670,000	14
Saskatchewan	(Can.)	251,700	921,000	4

POLITICAL DIVISION OR REGION		AREA IN SQ. MILES	POPULATION 1960 EST.	POPULATION PER SQ. MI.
Saudi Arabia		617,600	6,159,000	9.9
Scotland	(Br.)	30,411	5,225,000	171
Senegal, Rep. of	(Fr. Com.)	76,153	2,337,000	30
Seychelles	(Br.)	156	47,500	304
Sierra Leone	(Br.)	27,925	2,185,000	78
Sikkim	(Ind. Prot.)	2,745	152,000	55
Singapore & Deps.	(Br.)	289	1,595,000	5,519
Solomon Is.	(Austl.)	4,100	58,000	14
Solomon Is.	(Br.)	11,500	106,500	9
Somalia	(Ital. Tr.)	178,155	1,367,000	7.6
Soudan (Sudanese Rep. (Fr. Com.)		465,050	3,748,000	8
South America		6,860,000	137,846,500	20
South Carolina	(U.S.)	31,055	2,444,000	79
South Dakota	(U.S.)	77,047	708,000	9
S. Rhodesia	(Rh. & Nya.)	150,333	2,640,000	17
S. W. Africa	(U. of S. Afr.)	317,725	608,000	2
Soviet Union	(U.S.S.R.)	8,599,600	212,801,000	24
Spain		194,345	30,090,000	154
Spain & Possessions		321,335	30,384,000	94
Spanish Guinea	(Sp.)	10,828	216,000	20
Spanish Sahara	(Sp.)	102,676	13,000	0.1
Sudan		967,248	11,549,000	11
Surinam	(Neth.)	55,198	254,000	4.6
Svalbard	(Nor.)	23,979	1,100	0.05
Swaziland	(Br.)	6,705	277,000	41
Sweden		173,577	7,468,000	43
Switzerland		15,937	5,246,000	329
Syria	(U.A.R.)	71,209	4,556,000	64
Tanganyika	(Br.)	362,688	9,052,000	25
Tennessee	(U.S.)	42,244	3,506,000	83
Texas	(U.S.)	267,339	9,689,000	36
Thailand		198,404	22,003,000	119
Tibet	(China)	469,194	1,699,000	4
Togo, Rep. of	(Fr. Com.)	22,002	1,136,000	51
Tokelau (Union of)	(N.Z.)	4	2,000	500
Tonga	(Br.)	269	62,000	230
Trucial Oman	(Br. Prot.)	32,269	91,000	2.8
Tunisia		48,319	3,987,000	82
Turkey		296,108	26,494,000	89
Uganda	(Br.)	93,981	5,892,000	63

POLITICAL DIVISION OR REGION		AREA IN SQ. MILES	POPULATION 1960 EST.	POPULATION PER SQ. MI.
Union of South Africa				
(Br. Comm.)		472,550	14,435,000	30
United Arab Republic		457,309	29,869,000	65
United Kingdom		94,214	52,402,000	556
United States		3,615,210	178,784,000	49
United States & Poss.		3,628,130	181,347,000	50
Upper Volta, Rep. of				
(Fr. Com.)		105,879	3,516,000	33
Uruguay		72,153	2,709,000	37
Utah	(U.S.)	84,916	902,000	11
Vatican City		0.2	1,050	5,250
Venezuela		352,051	6,622,000	18
Vermont	(U.S.)	9,609	375,000	39
Vietnam, North		61,516	14,788,000	240
Vietnam, South		65,709	12,988,000	197
Virgin Is.	(U.S.-Br.)	200.2	40,300	201
Virginia	(U.S.)	40,815	4,084,000	100
Wales	(Br.)	8,016	2,991,000	373
Washington	(U.S.)	68,192	2,836,000	42
Western Samoa	(N.Z.)	1,133	106,000	93.5
West Indies	(Br.)	8,005	3,279,000	410
West Virginia	(U.S.)	24,181	1,960,000	81
Wisconsin	(U.S.)	56,154	4,053,000	72
World		52,125,000	2,930,050,000	56.2
Wyoming	(U.S.)	97,914	325,000	3
Yemen		75,270	4,900,000	65
Yugoslavia		98,740	18,796,000	190
Yukon	(Can.)	207,076	14,000	0.06
Zanzibar	(Br.)	1,026	178,000	173

INDEX